"You're different now," she murmured

Lynn stared up at her husband through moist lashes, savoring the feel of his body next to hers. The staggering truth that she wanted only to remain like this, secure in the comfort that, incredibly, he could give her, suddenly hit her.

"If y-you were—always l-like this...." What was she trying to say? How could she be content so close to the strong, hard body that had inflicted such insults on her own? "Why are you acting differently toward me?" she asked softly.

To her surprise, Rad shook his head sadly and those black eyes seemed to become dulled by regret.

"I can't explain," he told her huskily. "No, my Lynn, I can't."

A deep frustration filled her. She feared she would never fully know the man who had led her through such a nightmare....

ANNE HAMPSON
is also the author of these

Harlequin Presents

25—BY FOUNTAINS WILD
28—DARK AVENGER
31—BLUE HILLS OF SINTRA
34—STORMY THE WAY
37—AN EAGLE SWOOPED
40—WIFE FOR A PENNY
44—PETALS DRIFTING
47—WHEN THE CLOUDS PART
51—HUNTER OF THE EAST
56—AFTER SUNDOWN
59—BELOVED RAKE
63—STARS OVER SARAWAK
72—THE WAY OF A TYRANT
79—THE BLACK EAGLE
87—FETTERS OF HATE
95—DARK HILLS RISING
108—PRIDE AND POWER
115—THE FAIR ISLAND
125—DEAR PLUTOCRAT
132—ENCHANTED DAWN
143—A MAN TO BE FEARED
152—AUTUMN TWILIGHT
168—DANGEROUS FRIENDSHIP
181—ISLE AT THE RAINBOW'S END
187—HILLS OF KALAMATA
196—FOLLOW A SHADOW
209—SONG OF THE WAVES
463—BRIDE FOR A NIGHT

ANNE HAMPSON

beloved vagabond

Harlequin Books

TORONTO • LONDON • LOS ANGELES • AMSTERDAM
SYDNEY • HAMBURG • PARIS • STOCKHOLM • ATHENS • TOKYO

Harlequin Presents edition published December 1981
ISBN 0-373-10470-7

Original hardcover edition published in 1977
by Mills & Boon Limited

Printed in U.S.A.

CHAPTER ONE

THE car travelled slowly along the coast road, its occupant trying to keep her mind on her driving while at the same time absorbing the beauty of the scenery—the rugged mountains and tree-clad foothills, the spectacular curve of the bay with its fretted rock formations rising above the lovely golden sands. Originally Lynn had planned to come to Southern Ireland with a girl friend but, let down only two days before they were due to depart, she had decided to come alone, bringing her car over on the ferry. She had toured for ten days, delighted with the beauties of the island, and it was only in the evenings she would feel a little lost and lonely when, having booked in at an hotel, she would have to dine alone. Now she was in Donegal, idling away an hour or two before going to the hotel. Tomorrow she would begin travelling south making her way leisurely, over the next few days, to Dun Laoghaire, where she would eventually get the ferry back to England.

Stopping the car in a narrow lane just off the main road, Lynn took out a guide book. But her mind was not on the words before her; she was thinking of the proposal of marriage she had received a couple of weeks ago. Thomas worked with her in the office; he was homely and kind, but, in the words of one of Lynn's colleagues, 'As dull and stolid as they come.'

Lynn, though, had promised to consider his proposal, one reason being that she had begun to dislike living on her own in her tiny bed-sitter with its poky kitchen at one end and its shared bathroom at the opposite side of the corridor. It would be nice to set up a proper home with someone who would be her friend and good companion, she kept on telling herself. However, Lynn freely admitted that her second reason for considering Thomas's proposal was that she felt sorry for him. He, like herself, was the victim of a broken marriage, and in consequence lived on his own. Lynn thought of her childhood and the security of a home where there was love. But when she was seventeen her parents had separated, having previously decided that if ever the time came when they began to get on one another's nerves, they would take the sensible course and dissolve the marriage. Within three years both had married again, Lynn's mother to an American who took her to his home in Boston, and her father to a lady who persuaded him to settle near her married brother in Brisbane, Australia. And so Lynn at twenty was entirely alone, her secure little world of love collapsed. And now at twenty-four she was still alone, not having met any man she could learn to love.

She gave a small sigh, pressed the starter, and drove along the lane, into an even narrower lane which was overhung with trees. As she progressed she came to a wooded area, with a pretty little lake to her right and, on her left, a few hundred yards ahead, a gipsy encampment. She smiled. These wandering tribes were far more numerous here than in England; to Lynn they were part of the atmosphere and she thought that if only they would not leave so much litter behind them they would enhance rather than detract from the rural scene.

Suddenly, just as she drew abreast of the first caravan, the engine spluttered and then went quiet. Lynn frowned, drawing in to the side and coming to a stop. Several small children were the first to come and stand by the car, then a couple of women appeared at the

'You ... brute!' She was freed at last, but the man stood close. Fear, deep and terrible, caused her fury to rage. She lashed him with her tongue, but he seemed quite insensible to the names she called him. And she knew without any doubt at all that he meant to do her irreparable harm.

He took hold of her again, laughing aloud at her struggles. And just as he was about to throw her on the ground a noise was heard—the cracking of a twig under someone's foot. The man, his grip bringing Lynn forward again so that her balance was restored, turned with a snarl and faced the black-haired girl whose eyes were like fire.

'Wait! So ... you are at it again!' The girl's mouth twisted with anger. 'Leave that girl alone!'

To Lynn's amazement the gipsy let go of her wrist. She looked down at the bruise, but even as she did so she started to run. Reaching her car, she hesitated, then raced past it, not stopping until, exhausted, she was on the main road.

Looking back on the incident a couple of days later Lynn marvelled at the way she had got over it, since at the time she was literally weak with fear. And yet when once escape was made possible she was given the strength to run and run until, having reached the main road, she was fortunate enough to catch a bus almost immediately. It took her to the hotel, from where she telephoned a garage. The following morning the car was delivered to her, the repair, which had proved to be a very minor one, having been done. Lynn had wasted no time in leaving the district and when once again she was on the road, exploring more of Ireland's spectacular scenery, the incident began to fade so quickly that it no longer troubled her.

She drove south, entering the lovely valley of Maam, on the most westerly point of Lough Corrib. The scenery, breathtaking in its immense variety of mountains, moorlands, lake and wooded hills, suited Lynn's mood in that the whole aspect was one of remoteness, of unspoiled isolation. She felt totally at peace, driving slowly through the valley, looking out for a guesthouse or, better still, a farmhouse where she could put up for the night. To her delight she found the latter, a small and lonely farm where, on a post at the gate of the yard, was displayed a sign, 'Bed and Breakfast'.

The farmer's wife smilingly showed Lynn to a room, furnished cosily in the old-fashioned style and spotlessly clean. From her window Lynn could view the mountains to one side and some thickly-wooded hills to the other. Something caught her eye, something like a chimney-stack picked out in the sunshine.

'Is there a house over there?' She pointed towards the wooded eminence. 'I thought I saw a chimneypot.'

'That's the stately home of Mr de Gais.' The woman's tone of voice had changed. It was still as friendly, but Lynn denoted a strange inflection as she added, 'He's the Lord of the Manor of all these lands. The house was once an abbey,' the woman went on, and now her voice had resumed its former tone. 'It's called Ballytara Abbey. It's a very beautiful house, set in the most delightful gardens—some of the ancient trees were planted when the building was in fact a monastery.'

'Are the gardens open to the public?'

'They are, yes—every Tuesday and Saturday during the summer.'

Lynn was interested.

'I love wandering round the gardens of stately homes,' she admitted with a laugh. 'May I book this room for two nights instead of one? I'd like to visit the gardens of Ballytara Abbey.'

'Of course you can book the room, for as long as you like, Miss Seldon. Apart from the Abbey there's a lot more to see around these parts.' The farmer's wife pointed. 'If you ride you can get a horse from the riding school just across the valley road.'

Lynn thanked her, keeping in mind what she had said about the riding school. Yes, it would be nice to ride in this beautiful valley, she decided. Meanwhile, she wanted nothing more than a bath; the weather had been exceedingly hot all day, with the result that Lynn had perspired despite the fact that she had had all the windows open to allow in the cooling breeze.

The farmer's wife provided an evening meal if it was required by her guests, and Lynn naturally ordered one. She entered the dining-room to find a young couple already there, talking quietly to the maid. They smiled, and soon Lynn was joining in the conversation. The maid went out, to return a short while later with the soup.

'Are we the only guests?' Lynn asked.

'No, there are four others—two young men and an older couple. They've all gone off together to dine at the Kenlare Hotel. It's about three miles from here and noted for its excellent food.' The man smiled, then introduced himself and his wife. 'But don't call us Mr and Mrs Austin,' he added, 'just Bob and Mary.'

'I'm Lynn—Lynn Seldon.'

'Are you here for long?'

'Two nights, that's all.' Lynn sat down at the table opposite to Mary. 'I want to see the Abbey gardens.'

'They're magnificent!' from Mary as she took up her soup spoon. 'We went over them on Tuesday; there seemed to be miles and miles of grounds surrounding the mansion.'

'I shall have to give myself plenty of time, then.'

'Indeed, yes. We started out immediately after lunch. The gardens are open only from two till five.'

Lynn set off at a quarter past one on the Saturday, following the valley road for some distance before beginning to climb gently with the gradient. After some time she found herself travelling alongside a wall at the end of which were a pair of ornate wrought-iron gates leading to a path flanked by two stone lodges, one at each side. A uniformed attendant waved her on and she automatically glanced at her watch. She was a little early and had expected to be kept waiting outside the gates. About halfway along the avenue was a small neat hut, with another uniformed attendant ready to take the money. This, Lynn was later to learn, was for charity, as the owner of the mansion did not require any of the proceeds for himself.

'Park on the green, over there,' said the attendant, offering Lynn two tickets, one for the gardens and one for the car park. 'The attendant will show you where to go.'

'Thank you.' Lynn drove on, parked the car as instructed, and then she was free to wander in the lovely tranquil woodland setting described to her by Mary and Bob Austin. They had not exaggerated. Everywhere she looked Lynn met with breathtaking beauty. There were leafy paths and lily ponds, streams tumbling over rocks and under little rustic bridges where bright green creepers converged on one another from the sides, often dangling their pendulous branches over the water. There was statuary and fountains, all with a profusion of flowers surrounding them. Lynn stopped several times to read the names of the shrubs and trees, and one little plaque told her that the formal terraces to the south front of the house had been designed by Muriel, wife of the second Viscount de Gais in the nineteenth century. She paused a long while to admire the house itself, noting the classical style of Renaissance architecture. Obviously the mansion had undergone extensive renovations in the eighteenth century, as it was at this time that the great houses of Ireland had adopted the style of architecture earlier designed by Palladio.

An American garden was reached unexpectedly after Lynn had progressed along an avenue of magnificent lime trees. In the garden exotic shrubs and trees flourished among the indigenous plants, and a display of magnolias was especially entrancing to Lynn, who stood there, absorbing the sheer undiluted beauty around her and thinking how fortunate were the owners of so magnificent a residence as Ballytara Abbey. Through a wrought-iron arch she glimpsed what she surmised to be the only remaining part of the original abbey—some crumbling ruins delightfully spangled with ivy and other attractive creeping plants.

At last it was time to go. Lynn had subconsciously been hoping to catch a glimpse of one or other of the owners—she had decided that the master of such a grand establishment must be married and, probably, the father of several children. But if the occupants of the house did happen to be at home they were keeping themselves well out of sight. The only people Lynn saw were other sightseers enjoying the sunny afternoon among the luxurious flowers and trees, the attendants, and a girl selling guide books at a little stall by one of the fountains.

Making her way out, Lynn found herself close to the west wing of the house. Several people—who appeared to be one family—were peering through a large picture window and, without actually intending to do likewise, Lynn nevertheless found herself moving towards them.

'That's his mother,' she heard one middle-aged lady say, pointing to a large oil painting on the wall facing the window.

'She was very beautiful!' from a younger woman who had pushed her way forward, entirely blocking Lynn's view.

'Such a pity she did what she did.'

'They say that her parents flew a black flag afterwards. She was dead as far as her family was concerned.'

'Yes, they sometimes do that here. She died anyway, soon afterwards, didn't she?'

'Yes, in childbirth.' There was a pause after that while the people peered through the window, one moving to allow another a good view. Extremely curious by this time, Lynn hovered about, waiting for them to move away.

'Did her parents take the child?'

'I'm not quite sure of the story—not really. These scraps of it have come to me at various times.' The speaker had a most attractive Irish burr, soft, musical 'like the murmur of a breeze against a wooded hill'.

'Well, whether her parents took the child or not he's here now, the proud owner of Ballytara Abbey.'

'And it was he who found the painting, thrust away by her parents in a damp old building which he has since had pulled down. He rescued the painting, had it restored, and hung it in this beautiful drawing-room, in a place of honour.'

'It's a sad story, isn't it?' This came from the youngest member of the party, a pretty girl of about eighteen years of age. 'How old is he now?'

'Oh ... about thirty, I should think.'

'Is he married?'

'No—that I do know, because there was some gossip a while ago about that film star—— Oh, what is her name? Yes, Miranda Roland! She was running after him, but he had no interest in her at all. Someone who used to work in the house here told Maureen that he was once heard to say that he would know at the first glance the woman he wanted for his wife.'

'Sounds like a romantic. It's said he's extraordinarily handsome, but in an unusual way.'

'Well, he's bound to be different, isn't he?'

'So sad, this lovely young girl dying so soon after her marriage...' The party were moving away and Lynn took a couple of steps forward.

'What exactly happened, Nan?'

'She ran off with a...'

They were out of earshot and Lynn heard no more. She glanced around before looking through the window, aware that it was not the thing to do. But her curiosity had been aroused and she just had to take a peep at the painting.

It fascinated her; she found herself quite unable to take the intended quick glance and come away. How very lovely! Dressed in a flowing gown of hand-made lace, with her golden hair falling in ringlets about her sloping shoulders, the girl looked every inch an aristocrat while at the same time giving the impression of gentleness, naïveté and total trust. Her sensitive mouth was parted in a smile, her large blue eyes were clear and glowing. She was certainly a happy girl at the time this painting was being executed.

'And to die in childbirth. Why do such things have

to happen?' Lynn began to walk away at last, but the story she had heard was so fixed in her mind that she felt she would never forget it. The child for whom the girl had given her life was obviously a boy, and it did Lynn's heart good to know he had rescued the picture of his mother and given it a place of honour in his home.

The following morning Lynn packed her bags and put them in the car. Then, after settling her bill and promising to stay at the farm the next time she came over, she drove to the riding stables, leaving her car in a small parking area some short distance along the road. Five minutes later she was looking at the pony brought to her by a stable-girl.

'Is she quiet?' Lynn had not ridden for some years and although she had by no means lost her confidence she did feel she ought not to take any risks with her mount.

'Very quiet. You'll be sorry to part with Fenella when you've finished your ride.' The stable-girl looked Lynn over appraisingly, noting the slender figure, the pearly fair skin, the hyacinth blue eyes and the luxurious dark hair held in place by a white Alice band which matched the white short-sleeved shirt which Lynn wore. 'You don't have jodhpurs with you?'

Lynn shook her head, glancing down at her navy-blue slacks, tight-fitting and drawn in at the waist by a belt of light blue suede.

'I'll be all right like this?'

'Certainly.'

A moment later Lynn was trotting across the field, heading for the woodland area in which the girl had advised her to ride. There were paths through the more densely parts of the wood, she had said, and there were also signs painted on trees here and there, so it seemed impossible to get lost.

The sun was shining, but within the woods only slanting rays of gold were to be seen, striking across the path and highlighting a small rivulet or stagnant pool.

'Oh, but this is heavenly!' Lynn laughed softly at the idea of being able to speak her thoughts aloud. Not a soul to be seen! It was as if she had the whole world to herself.

'Right, Fenella, you can have a rest. We'll stop here where you can crop the grass.'

The horse whinneyed and again Lynn laughed. It was all so still and quiet that the noise echoed through the forest.

'You're very sweet! The girl was right when she said——' Lynn stopped abruptly, nerves tingling. She had tethered Fenella to a tree and already the horse was cropping the grass at its feet. What was the sound she had heard? Looking around, Lynn could see nothing, yet she experienced the weight of fear born of uncertainty. For that sound had had some origin; there was another person besides herself in these dark and lonely woods. She knew instinctively that she was being watched and she glanced fearfully around. Nothing but the slight flutter of a leaf caught in the breeze...

And then a horse whinneyed! With trembling fingers she began to free her own horse, but before she had time to mount her the other horse came into view, led by ... the gipsy. Terror caught at Lynn's throat even while her mind tried to cope with the several baffling facts which the appearance of the man presented. How had he got here? Surely, with only horses as his means of travel, he could not have come this far? Gipsies she had seen always appeared to be travelling in the most leisurely manner; they had no need to hurry anyway, since they moved only from one night stop to another. And what of that beautiful horse he was leading? It was a gleaming, perfectly-groomed chestnut gelding.

Lynn's eyes moved to the man's face. He had come to a halt and was looking at her; she expected to see that fire in his black eyes, that cruelty about his mouth. Instead, she found herself forgetting everything in the amazement of noting certain things that, somehow, had previously escaped her. She saw the fine bone structure, just as she had done previously, but now she could see a nobility in his features, a refinement, in fact. The mouth seemed not so thin, the jaw, though taut, was less menacing. Her eyes moved to the hand holding the bridle—long and slender and incredibly well kept! What had the gipsy done to himself? His clothes were not the same either, although he was wearing the black sweater and the scarf—no, not the same scarf, for this one was clean, and it was a different colour from the other. He wore a pair of dark blue denims, whereas the other day he had been wearing filthy corduroys.

He must have stolen the horse! Also the clothes ... but what about those well-kept hands?

He was still looking at her, the most odd expression in his gaze. He might almost have been mesmerised, she thought.

'Good morning.' He spoke at last and the spell was broken. Lynn, terror and fury mingling to set her whole body shaking, managed to assess her chances of escape. The path was not too far away, and if she raced she could soon reach the open field which was part of the riding-stables. With a swiftness that amazed her she swung on to the horse's back, viciously striking out with her crop at the same time. She would pay him out for that attack! And at the same time she would delay his mounting his horse.

'Take *that*!' The crop struck him on the cheek and she saw his expression of disbelief, saw his hand touch the place where the whip had cut his flesh. 'You gipsy vagrant!' She was on fire with fury, wanting only to be revenged for his inexcusable treatment of her a few days ago. 'How dare you speak to me! Get back to your own kind!' she flung at him over her shoulder. 'Keep away from *decent* people!'

She raced through the woods hoping to find the path, feeling almost in a state of collapse, so consuming was her anger. But fear was there too and it provided the impetus to dig her heels into Fenella's flanks and urge her on to greater speed. How had that gipsy managed to get here? she asked herself again, the thudding of hooves from behind increasing her fear to real terror. If he should catch her now... She would receive no quarter! He would murder her and leave her lying here, in this lonely forest.

But what would he do to her *before* he murdered her...?

The sound of hooves was coming closer and Lynn, sick with fear created by her own picture of her fate, again dug in her heels, speaking to the horse as she did so. Even in this emergency she could not bring herself to use the whip on the horse. No, Fenella was far too gentle for that kind of treatment——

'Stop!' The command was a snarl of fury carried through the blanketing effect of the trees. 'Stop, I say!'

For answer Lynn swung her crop in the air, then raced on. But where was the path?

'Oh, God, I've missed it!' Terror choked her; perspiration dripped from her forehead and ran down on to her face. 'Help me! Someone help me!'

Fenella was tiring. Twice she stumbled, sending her rider forward and making her cry out in fear.

Thud ... *thud* ...! The gipsy was close; the very earth shook at his approach. Lynn cried out in despair, tears mingling with the sweat running down her face. He was almost abreast of her and she could imagine a snarling vicious profile.

'Stop, or I'll bring you to the ground!'

Lynn went on, ignoring the command, her fingers clenched on the reins. She thought that if she did come out of this alive the memory of it would haunt her all her life.

'Go away! Leave me alone!' she cried, racing wildly on. Her Alice band went in the wind and her hair streamed out behind her. 'The police will get you——!' Lynn's words were cut as the gipsy came alongside her; she saw the evil profile, and blood spilling from the wound she had inflicted. A long slender hand swept out in front of her to grasp the reins, but Lynn held on and for what seemed an eternity she and the gipsy galloped on, neck and neck, Lynn urged by fear alone, and her pursuer by a fury that seemed to communicate itself to her, warning her that she was doomed. 'Leave me alone!' she cried again, her head spinning as the trees passed dizzily before her eyes, numberless trees, unceasing! Oh, *where* was the path! A moan escaped her. There was no hope, for she was being forced deeper and deeper into the forest.

The end was inevitable, since Fenella was tiring rapidly whereas the gelding seemed as fresh as when the wild careering through the forest began. The gipsy jerked the reins out of Lynn's hands and within seconds he had brought the horses to a halt. Another few seconds saw him on the ground and, reaching up, he brought Lynn down in front of him. She faced him, a towering giant, his swarthy face twisted by fury. He put up a hand to his cheek; it was covered with blood when he drew it away. Lynn saw his expression and all hope fled. He spoke, asking if it were her horse. Surprised, she answered at once, telling him that Fenella was from a riding school. To her further surprise he nodded, as if he knew the school. The man looked down into Lynn's face, and it seemed like an eternity before he spoke again, this time saying,

'She'll find her way back, then,' and with that he gave the pony a slap on the flank and she turned, soon to disappear from sight.

'You,' he said, his face twisting into evil lines, 'where are you from?'

'England,' she answered, even while recalling that he himself had previously remarked that she was English. 'I'm on holiday here. I've been staying at a farmhouse—over there,' she told him quiveringly, scarcely able to think, so great was the fear that engulfed her.

The gipsy nodded thoughtfully and she wondered if he knew the farmhouse as well as the stables. Gipsies wandered about so much that it would not really be surprising if he did know the area.

'You said "I'm" on holiday. Does that mean that you're on your own?'

'Yes, that's right. I'm touring in a car. It's parked not far from the stables.'

'You're touring, you say? Have you booked out of the hotel this morning?'

'Yes.'

He continued to ask questions which Lynn answered automatically; it did not register in her dazed and terrified mind that he was gaining knowledge which she ought at all costs to have kept to herself. It was only when she heard him say, very quietly,

'All alone here...' that she understood what she had done. Anger rose, with the result that when he asked why she had struck him with her crop she answered, deep contempt in her tone,

'Because you and your kind are the dregs of society——' But she instantly regretted her temerity. It was the height of folly to enrage him any more than he was enraged already. His face came close, evil, leering.

'The dregs, eh!' And with a savage sweep he had taken her up and flung her on to the horse's back. In a flash he was up behind her and the gelding seemed to have been endowed with wings.

The trees flashed by; the forest was becoming even darker as the horse entered into the thickest part. Lynn repeatedly asked what the man meant to do with her, where he was taking her, but she received no answer. Fury, vibrant and unquenchable, emanated from him, transmitting itself to her consciousness, a deadly warning of a fate too terrible to contemplate.

The loneliness was suffocating now, whereas before it had been a real joy to her. The man's arms and his body nauseated her, so close were they to her own body. His breath, surprisingly clean and cool, touched her throat and sometimes her cheek. She shuddered over and over again, and gave a little silent moan now and then, wondering what she had done to deserve a fate such as this. Her nerves had almost reached snapping point when at last he decided to break the silence.

'We're going to my camp. We're nearly there.'

'Your—your c-camp?' Terror edged her voice. He laughed harshly, without humour.

'Yes, my camp. It's on the far side of this forest.'

'You'll be sorry for this! The police are bound to get you, to arrest you. Aren't you afraid?' Stupid question! A man like this knew no fear. He was a law unto himself, a man free to follow the custom of his tribe; that was all he would ever know about such things as the laws of a country.

'Afraid?' The gipsy laughed again, throwing back his curly head. 'I've never been afraid of anything!'

'You'll never get away with abduction!' she burst out when presently, through a gap in the trees, the gipsy camp came into view. 'You're a fool to believe you can!'

He made no answer, remaining arrogantly aloof—as if she were far beneath his attention. Lynn, scanning the dark faces as she and the man arrived at the camp, failed to recognise any of those people she had seen before. Nor did any of them appear to recognise her as the girl whose car had broken down by their camp.

'Radulf!' The cry of welcome issued from several pairs of lips at once. Lynn, half dazed though she was with fear, gained the impression that the man Radulf had been away from the camp for some time. Did he not belong to any one camp? This was obviously not the camp at which she had first encountered him. 'But who is this?' A swarthy-skinned man came forward, eyeing the girl up in front of Radulf. 'It is not like you to——' His words were cut abruptly by a warning lift of Radulf's hand. Several voices were heard at once, as Radulf swung down from the saddle.

'Your face! What have you done to it?' Mostly, the words were in English, but some were spoken in Romany. Lynn guessed that those people speaking their own language were asking the same question. Radulf's swarthy features became a mask of hate, and those black eyes glittered their warning as they rested on Lynn's ashen face. He had reached up with both hands; she shuddered as those hands gripped her waist, then slid insolently to her breasts as she put her feet on the ground. Laughter went up, but there was puzzlement too on some of the brown faces. Were these people thinking of Radulf's gipsy girl-friend and wondering where she was?

Radulf spoke in Romany and Lynn felt sure he was inventing some explanation for the livid red weal on his cheek. The blood was beginning to cake, but it had previously flowed freely and the stains were hard and dry on his neck before disappearing into the roll-collar of his black cotton sweater. What an outlaw he looked! A swashbuckler who flaunted man-made rules and followed his own primeval instincts. What mercy could she expect from such a man? She tried not to dwell upon what was so obviously in store for her, but like some sinister dark cloud it enveloped her whole mind so that she actually began to live through the outrages which this dark vagabond meant to inflict on her soft white body. If only she could die! Would he kill her in the end—slowly strangle her with those slender brown hands that seemed so sensitive in appearance but, Lynn felt sure, held an immensity of hidden strength?

Radulf and the man who had first spoken had fallen into a deep conversation. Lynn heard the names 'Olave' and 'Albán' spoken several times. She soon gleaned the information that the man was Olave and that they were discussing someone else called Albán. Wherher Albán was a man or woman Lynn could not have said, but she felt that Albán was more a masculine name than a feminine one. Watching her captor's face intently, she saw that he was gravely troubled, and that he was conveying his anxiety to his listener who, nodding repeatedly, pursed his lips at last and gave a sigh.

After a time the men's conversation was brought to

an end by impatient questions, spoken in Romany, coming thick and fast, from the tribe of gipsies standing by. Plainly their patience had been exhausted, and even the little brown children, some half naked, others in ragged clothes often too small or too large for them, were murmuring and pulling at Radulf's denims. He sent forth a few answers, his expression a mingling of impatience and, amazingly, a sort of cool hauteur. But suddenly his whole manner underwent a change, a change that brought a gasp to Lynn's lips. For at one moment he had been serious, anxious, his voice low and almost cultured; now he was the outlaw, eyes gleaming with humour but beneath which was the dark threat of passion held in check. Without more ado he swung his half-fainting captive into his arms—and for one unbearable, humiliating second Lynn thought he would fling her across his shoulder like a sack of potatoes. She was carried, amid laughter and chanting, to a caravan which had previously been indicated by the man Olave. As he thrust her through the open door Lynn managed to marshall the strength to turn to the laughing crowd and shout,

'This man's abducted me! You are all criminals if you do nothing to help me!' She looked round, despairingly, at the enigmatic faces, brown, dirty faces, framed by dank black hair. 'I demand help——' No more. The door banged in her face and the laughter rose again. No one, then, was going to interfere with anything that Radulf did. He seemed like a king among them, since they had all appeared to be a little awed by his presence despite their laughter, and their rude interruptions when he was speaking so seriously to Olave.

The tears came, released from the cloud behind her eyes. She turned slowly from the door, to examine her small prison. A couch across one narrow end and a table by a small window, with two high stools beside it. The floor, devoid of covering other than three small hand-made rag rugs, was badly in need of a scrub. There was a brass oil lamp on a small, rickety book-case. Lynn's eyes naturally came in the end to settle on the largest of the three windows. Not very promising, and yet she felt sure she could manage to squeeze through it, were the opportunity to present itself. But despair soon erased that tiny thread of hope; the gipsy had not brought her this far to let her escape him. Out there people milled about, obviously still discussing the appearance of Radulf. What was his other name? Lynn wondered. Perhaps gipsies did not have sur-names. For a second or two she found herself thinking of this other man, this Albán of whom they had been speaking, and for no apparent reason she was most curious to know just what Radulf and Olave had been saying about him.

CHAPTER TWO

LYNN turned at last from her contemplation of the window and, noticing an alcove at the far end of the caravan, she went towards it, then through it. A tiny kitchen with a plastic sink and a butane stove, thick with grease and dirt. Nauseated, she was about to return to the living part of the caravan when she caught the clear sound of voices. The window, not more than six inches square, was actually open! Radulf and Olave were talking again, apparently having been given some privacy—perhaps Radulf had *ordered* the rest of the tribe to keep away. It was the kind of thing which Lynn could imagine his doing. The men were speaking in English, Olave addressing Radulf as Rad, in the most friendly and familiar way. Lynn, scared that she might be seen if she looked out of the window, kept to one side, even crouching a little, keeping her head beneath the level of the bottom of the window.

'It *is* worrying for you, Rad, but after all, the life he has chosen——'

'Is not the life he should be leading!'

'I agree, and I too have searched, as you asked me to. He's so elusive. You hear he's somewhere one day, but the next day he's gone. I recently had news of him—as I mentioned a few moments ago when we were talking over there—but when I arrived at the camp he was gone.'

'He went abroad at one time, as you know.'

'He's back in Ireland now.'

'I'm aware of that,' said Rad impatiently. 'I

wouldn't be here if he wasn't! I'd heard he was here. Ivarr phoned to tell me.'

'You were coming here when you picked up the girl?'

'Of course. Why else would I be dr——' Rad stopped for some reason and Lynn was left trying to finish the word he had begun to say. Could it be 'dressed'? If so, what would be likely to follow?

'Why else would I be dressed like this?' Was that what she would have heard, had Radulf finished the sentence?

Lynn shook her head, wondering why she listened at all, since nothing made any sense—and why should it, when it was no concern of hers?

Olave was speaking again, saying something about 'the girl'.

'You'll not seduce her?' Lynn heard the man add.

'Not?' with a sort of harsh mockery. 'That wench is going to pay dear for striking me with that whip, and calling me a vagrant gipsy, the dregs of society!'

'People who are not gipsies have strange ideas about us, Rad. Perhaps you should make excuses.' So mild was this man's voice, so tolerant his outlook. Lynn warmed to him even though she cherished no wild dreams of enlisting his help. He was obviously a very good friend of Rad and would therefore turn a blind eye to anything which Rad chose to do.

'I make excuses for no one—man or woman—who thinks fit to insult me!'

'She looks to be a decent girl. Are you willing to ruin her?'

Lynn was puzzled, as it did seem that Olave was exceedingly surprised that Radulf would seduce a decent girl ... or any girl for that matter. Well, it would seem that Olave did not really know his friend, as for a certainty he had meant mischief on that first occasion when he had grabbed hold of Lynn, kissed her and then was about to throw her on the ground when, luckily for Lynn, his gipsy girl-friend had come upon the scene. Of course, the girl could have been Radulf's wife, but Lynn felt sure she wasn't, especially in view of the conversation going on out there now. She felt that Olave would have made his protest much more strongly had his friend been married.

'I intend to exact reparation from her, and if she happens to be ruined in the process then it will teach her a lesson.' Inflexible the tones, and Lynn knew that nothing she could do or say would weaken his resolve. She supposed a man with such primitive instincts would never understand that it was only natural that she should have wanted to pay him back for his fiendish attack on her.

'She said you'd abducted her, and it's plain that you have,' Olave was saying in that mild and slow manner of speaking. 'Abduction's an offence for which you can expect to pay dear. You have your position to think of, Rad. It isn't worth it. You always were a hothead with a vicious temper, but I should have thought you'd long since have learned to curb it.'

Your position ... Lynn's forehead creased. What position? Was Radulf the head of the tribe? But this was not his particular tribe. Perhaps he was the 'king' of all the gipsies in this country. Yes, that would explain the word 'position' and also the respect with which those people out there treated him. It might also explain why he went about from one camp to another.

'I'll pay dear, you think? Well, I never was one to count the cost, was I?' A harsh laugh broke and the words following seemed to be lost in its echo. Lynn wondered how many other girls he had assaulted; and, it would seem, he had escaped without punishment. 'I shall think of something, so don't worry about me, Olave, my friend.'

'I feel responsible, because I always knew——'

'But in the end you spoke. Olave, you are old; don't spend your last few years in self-condemnation. I guess I would have done the same myself.'

'It does my heart good to hear you say so, Rad. And yet, when I see you like this, caring nothing for your outlawry, snatching a young girl and carrying her off—well, I must blame myself, mustn't I, and dwell on what would have happened if I had spoken sooner?'

'You could not speak sooner, not until she had died.'

Lynn, fascinated now by the conversation she was so clearly overhearing, forgot for a brief space her own terrible position. There was something which savoured of a tragedy here. And it seemed that if Olave had spoken sooner then Radulf, his friend, would not have been quite so wicked as he now was. Spoken sooner about what?

'You're generous, Rad.' A small silence followed and then, in a soft persuasive tone of voice, 'The girl ... I'm sorry for her——'

'Then you needn't be! She's asked for what she's going to get!'

What a change in the timbre of his voice! Before, he had spoken with a refinement that was totally at variance with his appearance and with the way he had treated Lynn; now, though, his voice matched to perfection his vagabond daring in abducting her.

'She's English, you said?'

'That's right.'

'Then she'll have been missed already, for surely she had people with her—her parents, perhaps?'

'As a matter of fact, she's all alone here.'

'Alone?'

'That's right; she's touring in a car.'

'Look, Rad, you can't do this——'

'I've already done it, my friend.'

'She'll be missed, I say!'

'Don't panic, Olave,' returned Radulf imperturbably. 'The girl booked out of the hotel this morning, so they're not expecting her back.'

'You said she had a car. Where is it?'

Radulf told him, repeating all he had learned from Lynn, and only then did she realise she had not only told him the number of her car, but that the door was unlocked and the key in the ignition.

The men seemed to move away a little because Lynn began to miss some of what was being said, but she did manage to get the gist of it. Radulf was telling Olave to take the horse somewhere and to collect the car and bring it to the camp. Radulf would do it himself, but he had other things to see to.

'Pick up the car as soon as you can, Olave,' Lynn heard. 'I don't want it standing there too long.'

'I don't like it, Rad. It's not you. Now if it were your...' The voices faded and Lynn heard no more.

What were they going to do with her car? Fool that she was to have given the gipsy all that information! Had she not done so then someone would soon have noticed that the car had been there a long time and reported it to the police. As it was, the gipsy was having it moved. But did he believe that every trace of her would be lost so easily? Lynn shook her head, thinking about her home in England and her job. If she did not appear at the office inquiries must very soon be made, and if she failed to pay her rent at the end of the month then her landlord was also going to do something. All her colleagues knew she had come on a touring holiday, so it did not seem possible that she could just disappear without the most extensive inquiries being made, both by the authorities in this country and in her own.

And yet ... the gipsy seemed so imbued with confidence that Lynn would not be in the least surprised if, somehow, he managed to come out of this escapade totally unscathed.

Where was he now? She would not put it past him to torture her by allowing her nerves to reach breaking point before he put in an appearance. Yet every minute that passed was like stolen time to her, as she did wonder if, after all, Olave would manage to persuade him to let her go. She could hear chatter from outside and it began to unnerve her. Her heart began to thud so violently that she felt physically sick. She put a hand to her breast, closing her eyes and praying for help. If only she had not been so rash as to strike the man then perhaps he would not have troubled her at all. But the calm way in which he had greeted her, just as if he had never seen her before, much less assaulted her, had aroused her anger, and this, along with the fierce desire to punish him, had caused her to act without thinking of what the consequences of her act might be. And now she was here, the prisoner of a fiend whose intention was to ruin her, here in a caravan among people without scruples, people who would not raise one finger to help her escape the fate planned for her by the man who had abducted her.

She tried the door, then hammered upon it. Both acts were foolishly unthinking, since she knew full well that they would have no effect. It was just that she felt she must do something, or she would find herself screaming, having succumbed to the nervous tension that had built up inside her.

Laughter rose outside, and a good deal of chatter was still going on. Lynn heard the name Radulf several times, and then merely Rad, this sometimes from Olave, spoken quietly; she recognised his voice. Lynn put her hands to her ears when presently she heard laughter again. She went over to a couch and sat down, rose again and walked over to one of the windows, pulling aside the curtain, which had been partly closed. Caravans, four of them, brightly painted. She had always admired these old-fashioned caravans, preferring them to the modern ones which were now the vogue among the gipsies. Admired ... Lynn felt she would never look upon a caravan again without reliving this terrible ordeal—if she came out of it alive, that was!

Footsteps! She froze, waiting, her eyes fixed on the handle of the door. It turned and at the same time she heard the key in the lock. Radulf came in, his black eyes flickering over her without interest. He was closing the door behind him, and again the key was turned, this time on the inside. Lynn watched him drop it into his pocket, saw him turn towards her, a towering figure far too large for this tiny space. He touched a sort of spring in the wall and a bed swung down, a bed ready made up, its covers fastened with tapes which Radulf proceeded to untie. He straightened up.

'Well,' he said in low detestable tones, 'we have come to the finale of our adventure.' He smiled without a trace of humour, and fingered the scar on his face. It had been washed, but the caked blood still covered part of the wound, which was vividly red and swollen. Lynn shuddered; she had never liked hurting people and the fact that she had been forced to use violence infuriated her. Rad spoke again. 'Come here,' he murmured, and pointed to a spot in front of him. 'You called me the dregs of society. Now you are to be punished. Come here, I said!' The scar seemed to become more livid as his fury rose.

Without waiting to see if she would obey him he snatched at her wrist, jerking her against his hard and muscular body. She shuddered, and began to struggle, but he held her without effort, his dark eyes smouldering as they looked down into hers. Lynn struggled again, heard his laughter, felt his hand arrogantly take hold of her hair. She cried out as he dragged her head right back so that the front of her neck was stretched as she was forced to stare into those compelling eyes. She saw his mouth move, sensuously, before his lips came down to meet hers. Powerless in the strength of his hold, she could only wait, steeling herself for the repetition of what she had suffered before. His kiss was cruel and masterful, his lips mercilessly crushing hers, forcing her own lips apart. His body pressed close, nauseating her. Tears flooded her eyes, blinding her, and when at length he held her from him his evil swarthy face was merely a blur. But to her surprise he produced a clean white handkerchief and dabbed it against her cheeks and eyes.

She lifted a hand to touch her bruised and swollen mouth, and suddenly she was conscious of the fact that there was something mysteriously different about his kisses this time; they were more passionate, more primitive and possessive, but that was not all. They were *less insulting* than before! Perplexed, she looked up. His features might have been etched in stone; his eyes too were unmoving. What, Lynn wondered, was occupying his mind at this time? What was the ceaseless play of thought behind that inscrutable countenance?

'Well,' he said at last, 'have you nothing to say before I take my full measure of revenge?' His black eyes glittered; his mouth was tight. 'I had at first intended paying you back in kind——' He swung a hand to where he had thrown down the riding-crop he had carried. 'Your face is too beautiful to mark——' Again he stopped, to lay a finger significantly on the scar she had made on his cheek. 'But your sides would have taken no harm. However, that kind of revenge did not appeal to me, after all. I find I have a much sweeter one in mind.' Radulf's smile was a sneer, the glimmer in his eyes a mark of triumph.

But he was hurt!

Lynn could *feel* that he was hurt. She had insulted him and he would never be able to forget it. She had called him the dregs of society, but he himself obviously thought otherwise, and he was determined to make her pay for the insult... and pay dear.

He spoke again, repeating what he had said at first.

'Have you nothing to say before I take my full measure of revenge?'

'You w-want me to beg—beg for mercy?' Her throat was so dry that she had the greatest difficulty in voicing her words.

'That, I'm afraid, wouldn't do you any good at all. I am not a merciful man.'

Lynn moved from him and stared through the window. Olave, mounted on the lovely thoroughbred gelding, was riding away from the camp.

'You—you can't possibly get away with this,' she quivered, trying not to cry again. 'You're bound to be punished.' Although white to the lips and shaking all over, she still clung to the tiny measure of courage left in her. 'When I'm free I shall go straight to the police.'

'It might be a long while before you are free.' Walking to a cracked mirror, he looked at his face. Lynn turned, swallowing convulsively as she saw the evil twist to his mouth. 'You're very beautiful; I believe I shall not tire of you very easily. Perhaps you will never be free—but time alone will tell.'

Never be free ... Could he keep her prisoner for the rest of her life? Lynn could not believe this to be possible and was about to scoff at the very idea when, with a great lurching of her heart, another idea came to her, an idea that had already occurred to her but had been forgotten. She said, forcing herself to phrase the question,

'What are you going to do to me?'

His eyebrows, straight and black, rose a fraction.

'Surely you don't require me to explain,' he answered in some amusement. 'If you do then you must be uniquely innocent.'

A flood of crimson took the pallor from her face.

'I meant—meant—afterwards——' She stopped, lifting a hand to her heart, for its violent thudding frightened her. 'If y-you intend—intend to—to k-kill me——?'

'Kill?' he broke in. He shook his curly head. 'What a waste that would be! No, my beauty, it isn't a lifeless corpse I want—on the contrary, I believe I shall find you vitally alive ... and responsive.'

'Responsive!' Lynn actually forgot her fear as anger flared within her. 'You'd do well to shed any illusions you have on that score! I have to admit to being in your power, but I am *not totally* so!'

'We shall see.' His arms went around her again and although instinct made her struggle, she was very soon exhausted by her futile loss of energy. 'Perhaps not at once, my beauty, but later ...' His mouth claimed hers, sensuously arrogant. 'After a day or two . . .' His hand was at her back, drawing her blouse out from the waist of her slacks. She felt the warmth of his flesh on her own, as his fingers caressed her back. His hand came round, slowly, to cup one firm breast against the palm. Lynn, weeping bitter tears, tried again to struggle, lashing out with her hand, and unintentionally scratching his scar with her fingernail, drawing blood. Fury leapt to his eyes and for the next few moments Lynn felt that all hell had been let loose. His primitive lovemaking drained her of every atom of strength; his mouth and body inflicted outrages on her own. His voice was hoarse with passion as, gripping the neck of her blouse, he told her she was about to have a demonstration of how the dregs of society treated their womenfolk.

'Oh, please! If I say I'm sorry——' The blouse was wrenched apart, the ripping of the material along the back sounding like the crack of a gun in the tiny space. Radulf, an outlaw and a vagabond, stood looking down at her heaving chest, his brown hands gripping the two sides of the blouse he had torn from her body.

'Sorry? You'll be more than sorry by the time I've finished with you——!' Tossing away the blouse, he swung her slender body into his arms and in two strides he reached the bed. Flinging her down, he again stood over her, his hands on his hips, his long legs astride. An outlaw, yes! A gipsy vagabond without scruples—a savage whose only thought was revenge.

And yet, as he stood there, so tall and powerful, his black head thrown back, there was something profoundly arresting about him. To her utter amazement Lynn was admitting that the man was handsome—though it was a wild and primitive kind of handsomeness, like that of a creature of the forest or jungle, noble yet untamed. His fine nostrils were quivering, his eyes fired with passion. There would be no restraint; he was the conqueror, the merciless avenger whose strength would vanquish any puny resistance she might decide to put up.

He laughed softly, his insolent gaze resting on the uncovered part of her body before lifting it to her face. Lynn, her cheeks on fire, lowered her lovely eyes in shame. The bed cover was beneath her, but she moved, releasing sufficient of it to hold against her, bringing it up to her chin. Her heart was racing, her every nerve chaotic. Surely death was preferable to this! And indeed she wished for one hysterical moment that he would come to her, curl those long brown fingers round her throat, and put her out of her misery. Tears hung on her lashes as she glanced up, curious to know why he hesitated so long. A sneer twisted his lips, but in his eyes a hint of humour gleamed.

'The torture is slow, eh? You did not contemplate this when you lifted that whip to my face, did you?' Humour had gone in a flash, blotted out by a venom that made Lynn gasp. The man was evil, and she wondered how anyone like Olave could have him as a friend. For although she had never spoken to the old man, she knew instinctively that he was good and kind. 'Unfortunately my patience cannot last,' he went on in a low and guttural tone of voice. 'If you weren't so desirable I'd enjoy prolonging the torture.' His eyes roved; he snatched at the bed cover, taking it from her grasp. 'The dregs of society!' Lynn heard his teeth grit together, watched him go over to each window, and, as he drew the curtains, a laugh went up from outside; Lynn put her hands to her ears.

'I hate you,' she whispered. 'If I could kill you I would.'

'Hate me?' Radulf laughed harshly. 'You'll hate me more yet, my girl! I'll have you crying out for mercy before I've done with you! Vagrant gipsy, am I?' Fury caused a hoarseness to edge his voice ... but it was the note of bitterness that caught Lynn's ears, bringing her eyes to his in a glance of sharp inquiry. He *was* a vagrant gipsy, so why should he be so bitter about it?

'I'll not be long,' he said in a low bass tone. 'My revenge is going to be exceedingly sweet.'

Lynn knew he was about to undress, knew he would then proceed to finish stripping her as well. She wept, great sobs racking her body ... wept and waited, resigned to her fate.

CHAPTER THREE

THE clamour outside, followed by a sharp knock on the door, brought Lynn from her half-dazed state and she sat up, holding the cover to her, hope leaping to her eyes.

'Something's wrong?' She stared at Radulf who, still fully dressed, was frowning darkly as he went to the door of the caravan. Before he could open it a sort of rhythmic chanting began and words were spoken in Romany. Suddenly he laughed, and flung wide the door. Two gipsy women stood there, while others pressed around them. Lynn, her embarrassment plain for everyone to see, could only stare, her heart thudding more loudly than ever, wondering what new and terrible fate was in store for her. Radulf spoke and was answered. A gay garment was thrust at him and he turned, holding it in his hands. That enigmatic look was over his face again, an unreadable mask that baffled Lynn. He was a deep thinker, this gipsy vagabond, a man whose mind was capable of dealing with every contingency in a cool and calculated way. All except his most primitive traits appeared to be fully under control. Lynn saw him nod thoughtfully, as if coming to a decision. He slid those black eyes to her face and said softly,

'And why not?'

'What's going on?' she demanded. Fear, renewed after that tiny spark of hope had flickered out, caused her voice to become high-pitched and almost hysterical. 'Tell me, I say!'

'A wedding, they are crying. My people—the dregs of society—are of the opinion that it is time I took to myself a wife.' He flung the garment at her, flung it into her face. 'They've brought you a wedding-dress. Put it on.'

'No!' Her face whitened but anger brought two little spots of colour to her cheeks. 'No one can force me into marriage against my will! Go away!' she screamed at those by the door. 'Go away—and take this with you!' She flung back the dress ... but knew without any doubt at all that she had made a mistake. Hostility took the place of laughter in the eyes of the gipsy women by the door. Radulf, too, was pale with fury. Slowly he stooped, to pick up the gaily-coloured dress. A single flick of a hand and the doorway was cleared. He kicked the door to, approached the bed and, laying down the dress, he pointed to it.

'Put it on,' he ordered quietly.

Lynn licked her lips, conscious of their parched state. An idea came to her and she said,

'Supposing I'm already married?'

Radulf's eyes were lowered to her left hand.

'I don't believe you are, but it would be of no matter. Put on the dress—if you don't want me to do it for you.'

Lynn's mind worked swiftly. If she obeyed him, and they went out there, she might be able to call for help...

'Very well.' She adopted an air of resignation. And, to deceive him further, she added meekly, 'I have no option but to marry you, and in any case, that will be preferable to—to being—er—er——'

'Taken without marriage?' he finished for her, laughter in his eyes.

'Can I have privacy while I change?'

'Whatever for? I'm your husband——'

'Not yet! Nor will you ever be, never in reality, that

is!' Her mind was still working on a means of escape. How far was the camp from the road? How loud could she shout? 'Please—I would like some privacy.'

Radulf looked at the cover she was holding against her chest.

'I've seen almost everything. Get off that bed and change! My people are waiting to celebrate my marriage.' He rose, because she made no move to obey his order. The next moment he had her on the floor. She said with resignation,

'Please sit down again. I'll do as you say.'

He watched her every move as she changed, laughing at her embarrassment. But yet she later saw an unfathomable light in his eyes that was neither amusement nor contempt. It could have been admiration!

The dress was full-skirted and long. And to Lynn's relief it was clean. She stood before her captor, watched his eyes flicker with interest as, rising, he reached out to take her hand.

'A kiss before we go,' he said, and pressed his lips to hers. 'Oh, by the way,' he added carelessly as he opened the door, 'what's your name?'

'My name...' Absurd as it seemed, Lynn had an hysterical desire to laugh. With only a few minutes to their marriage, her prospective bridegroom was casually asking her name! 'It's Lynn,' she said as he waited.

'Lynn. Hmm, pretty. Lynn—what?'

'Seldon.'

'You know mine. I prefer to be called Rad, not Radulf.'

'I shan't call you anything!'

'You'll do as you're told,' he stated. 'The first thing a gipsy wife learns is obedience. Come, my people are waiting!'

Once outside the caravan Lynn looked for the road. It was not too far away and her heart leapt with hope. If only someone would come walking past she would shout so loudly that they must hear her. And once she had arrested their attention it should not be difficult to enlist their help.

Alas for Lynn's hopes! The gipsies surrounded her; the man performing the ceremony was ready. To Lynn everything to do with the wedding was hazy, for disappointment flooded her being as her hopes shattered and then died altogether.

Was she legally married to this outlaw? she was asking herself a short while later. Somehow it did not seem to matter any more. She was his prisoner, his slave until he tired of her, and then perhaps release would come.

'No, not till he tires of me! I shall escape! Every moment of every day shall see me on the alert! He can't keep a watch on me all the time!'

'Come, my wife. We are to be escorted to the—er—bridal chamber.' He was laughing while Lynn seethed. Strangely, her fear was stilled and it was fury that engulfed her. 'Give me your hand.'

She put her hands behind her back and the gipsies laughed. Rad reached down and took Lynn's hand, then playfully slapped it. More laughter; some dancing and singing as the couple were accompanied to the caravan. At last the door was closed and Lynn, who had started out on holiday less than a fortnight ago, found herself alone with her vagabond husband.

The sun slanted through a chink in the curtains and Lynn opened her eyes. Memory surged through her, a deluge of humiliation and despair. She supposed that if she had not been so foolish as to struggle, and to call her husband an uncouth gipsy, he might have treated her with a little less cruelty. But she had aroused his fury and in consequence had suffered, being forced to endure a lovemaking that was primitive, masterful and totally lacking in respect. Rad had been determined to conquer her and he had succeeded. What he had failed to succeed in was her total surrender. He had tried hard enough to bring that about and she strongly suspected that her resistance had deflated his ego. She would probably suffer for that later, but for the present her own ability to resist him gave her at least some modicum of satisfaction.

She sat up, her eyes seeking the dark head on the pillow beside her. So tranquil! So harmless—almost like a little boy in the depth of the peace written into his features. Lynn felt an urge to slap his face, rudely to awaken him. Why should he sleep so peacefully when she herself had lain awake far into the night, living again the ordeal through which this husband of hers had put her?

He stirred at last, turning his head and appearing for one split second not to be able to take in where he was—or who he was with.

'Good morning,' he bade her presently. 'I trust you slept well?'

'Please tell me what we do now? I mean, am I to live here, with these people?'

'Where else? Wives usually live with their husbands, don't they? Or perhaps in England they live with someone else's husband?'

She turned away, wishing she had seized the opportunity and got up and dressed before he awoke.

'I shan't be able to find anything to do here.'

'You'll look after your husband for the present.'

'For the present?'

'Until the children come. Gipsies have them by the dozen, but I guess you will have noticed?'

She coloured.

'I hope I never have any children!' Suppose she did? How then would she escape? Perhaps, she thought with a flood of despair, she was already having a baby.

'You'll have children,' her husband told her. 'Because it is my wish that you shall.' His voice had dropped and he seemed to be carried away by abstracted thought. 'Every man wants an heir and I am no different from the rest.'

'An heir!' she ejaculated. 'What, pray, do you have to give to an heir?'

He sat up, eyes glinting, dangerously.

'Shall I give you a very excellent piece of advice, Lynn?' She said nothing, naturally, and he continued, 'Be careful you don't anger me too much. I assure you you haven't yet seen the worst of me.'

'Then God help me if ever I do!'

'Precisely.' Rad looked imperturbably at her, noting her set profile. 'Contrary to what you have decided, I do have something to leave my heir——'

'This—caravan! You poor creature! What is it worth——?' Lynn got no farther, her words cut by the cry of pain she made as Rad caught at her arm.

'You take too much for granted, my girl. I advise you not to speculate on my possessions!' His grip tightened. 'It would seem that I shall have to school you, wife——' His own words were cut as she wrenched herself from his grasp. But she was not quick enough in her intention of slipping out of the bed, which she would have had to do via the foot, as her side was close to the wall of the caravan. Rad caught her and before she knew it his ruthless arms were about her, his mouth fastened to hers. She felt a pain shoot through her head, knew a moment of despair before, resigned, she succumbed without resistance to his lovemaking.

'Well, have you come by now to regret what you did?' he was asking her later as they sat at the table having a breakfast of porridge and tinned milk. He was regarding her attire with a faintly amused expression and she snapped her teeth together. She was wearing the 'wedding' dress, since her blouse was quite beyond repair.

'You deserved it!' she flashed. 'And you know it!'

'Deserved it?' He looked so surprised that she wondered for a moment if he had forgotten that attack he had made on her.

'A filthy gipsy coming near me, and attempting to——' The tipping of the small table cut her short. Rad leapt to his feet, eyes blazing with fury. Lynn, cursing herself for her lack of caution, backed away from him, her heart beating overrate, her whole body shaking.

'You'll apologise for that!' he snarled, advancing slowly towards her. White to the lips, Lynn stared into the most evil face she had ever seen. 'And you'll do it humbly!' His hand shot out; Lynn was brought with a painful jerk towards him. He was consumed with rage as, gripping her arms with the pressure of a vice, he shook her so violently that he himself was breathless when at length he stopped. Lynn, almost fainting, and with tears streaming down her face, made the silent wish that she could die. To be in the power of such a fiend ... and with no hope of an early escape. 'Well,' he said grittingly, his temper abating a trifle, 'I'm waiting!'

Lynn needed no further persuasion to do his bidding. Through parched lips she framed her apology.

'I'm sorry. I shouldn't have said it——' She broke off, weeping unrestrainedly. The injustice of it was almost as painful mentally as his treatment of her physically had been. He *did* deserve all that she had said and done to him, and yet she was forced into apologising in this meek and servile manner. She looked up into his dark face, seeing the noble lines, the arrogance that gave him a certain arresting superiority. Anyone would think he was a lord rather than a gipsy vagabond! The air which he assumed, the aristocratic bearing ... So strange, in a gipsy ...

'You're wise to apologise,' he told her harshly. 'Any further persuasion would have left you smarting for a month!'

He released her, glancing at the table. Everything that had been on it lay scattered on the floor. Lynn shuddered, nauseated by the dirt. Rad, pointing to the debris, told her brusquely to pick it up. And although fury rose, bringing a swift retort to her lips, she was too wise to do anything but obey him.

'And you can get me some more breakfast,' he ordered, sitting down on the couch and stretching his long legs out before him. 'And put some salt in the porridge this time.'

She bent to gather up the plates and cutlery, then fetched a cloth to wipe up the spilled porridge. Tears rolled down her face so that she could scarcely see what she was doing.

After breakfast Rad informed her that he would be going out.

'Out?'

'I shan't be back all day,' he said, ignoring her one brief word. 'Don't get any ideas about escape; the caravan's being watched all the time.' He glanced around. 'I shall expect to see this place cleaned up when I get back.' He stopped, his eyes glinting as he noticed her chin lift a fraction. 'If you don't want a dose of your own medicine, then I advise you to do as I say.'

She had no need to ask him what he meant. One look at the scar was warning enough. But her blood boiled and it was some considerable time before she did get down to the task he had given her. Yet, once started, the cleaning up was not really a chore. After all, it was for her own benefit as much as his. She began with the furniture, which was badly scratched and could never look decent no matter what was done with it. However, when she had washed it with soap and water, and rubbed it with a duster she found in a cupboard under the sink, it did look much better. The floor was next; in places she had actually to get a knife and scrape the dirt away. Imagine anyone being happy to live with such filth, she thought, and stopped what she was doing and rose from her knees. Rad, she suddenly realised, had frowned once or twice when looking at the floor. He seemed out of place here ... A square peg ...

She sat on the couch, clasping her hands in front of her, thinking deeply, trying to recollect various little instances when she had been surprised by something her husband had done or said. His voice, for one thing; it had most attractive timbre of refinement for most of the time. Only when he was angry did it sound rough and uncouth. She tried to recall his voice on that first encounter, but was unable to do so, either when he was asking about the car, or later, which was not in the least surprising as, for one thing, he had said so very little to her—being more concerned with actions!—and for another, she herself had been so terrified that nothing registered other than his evil intent. Lynn brought other things to mind: the beautiful horse he had been riding, then the puzzlement she had felt because it had seemed impossible to have got so far in so short a time. She had driven for hours, and at a fair speed ... and yet he had done the same distance on a horse. True, he had taken longer, but that was no real explanation. It just could not be done in the time, she was soon telling herself. This meant that he had not come on the horse, but had used some faster means of transport. Perhaps he had travelled by bus.

Sighing heavily, more frustrated than anything else, Lynn resumed her scrubbing of the floor. The rugs were filthy and it took her all her time to handle them. Should she open the window and shake them? She shirked contact with any of the gipsies, even verbal contact, and yet it seemed a shame to put the rugs on to the clean floor without making some attempt to get the dust out of them.

But no sooner had she appeared at the window than a youth of about twenty years of age appeared. He was handsome in a rough kind of way, and when he opened his mouth it was to reveal the most even white teeth she had ever seen.

'I want to shake these rugs,' she said, hoping he understood English. He nodded, saying he would shake them for her.

'Thank you.' She handed them to him through the window, unaware that he was fascinated by her sad eyes and quivering mouth, or that he had never stopped thinking about her since the moment Rad had brought her to the camp and he had looked into her lovely face. 'It's your task to keep a watch on this caravan, I suppose?' she could not help saying as he handed the first rug back to her.

He nodded his dark head.

'I am sorry,' he murmured in his rough but quiet voice.

'Don't worry about it. I expect you have to do as Rad tells you?' She was fishing now, watching his expression intently.

'Everyone does as Rad tells them.'

'He—is the king of the gipsies?'

'Don't ask me questions, lady. I dare not answer them.' He shook the second rug and put it through the window. Lynn's eyes caught sight of a face peering from the caravan directly opposite, and then another at a second caravan. The boy turned as he saw her expression and hastily began shaking the third rug.

'I must go,' he said urgently after handing it to her. 'Please close the window and fasten it.'

'Not yet! Tell me your name?'

'Connell. They all call me Conn.' Again he glanced around. 'I must go. Those women will tell Rad that I was speaking to you.' He gestured urgently and she closed the window.

Help, she thought as she laid the rugs on the newly-cleaned floor, could come from that quarter...

Much later she again opened the window, this time doing it very quietly, after making sure that no one was anywhere near the windows of the other caravans. Conn approached after glancing all around.

'I want some water.' Lynn held up a can. 'Would you be so kind as to fetch me some?'

He did as she asked, but spoke no word as he handed the can up to her. Her eyes met his and she thought she saw deep admiration in his gaze. She looked at his clothes and felt sorry for him. It seemed all wrong that a young man like that should be living this kind of aimless existence.

'Thank you very much.' Lynn spoke softly, relieved

to see that no one had yet come prying to their doors or windows. 'What would happen to you if I got away from here?' she asked.

'I should be in trouble.'

'From my husband?'

'From him, yes. He has told me to stand guard over this caravan.'

Lynn found herself puzzled in some indefinable way which prompted the question,

'Does my husband intend to pay you for doing this?'

Colour edged beneath the boy's burnt-ochre skin. Her query had obviously embarrassed him. But he nodded and said yes, Rad would be paying him for standing guard like this.

'I need the money,' added Conn as if pleading with her to understand. He glanced around. 'I had better get you some more water,' he said. 'Have you another container?'

'Yes, I'll fetch it.'

Lynn handed it over, watching him out of sight. She wondered where he was getting the water, but did not let the matter occupy her mind for long. Swiftly she searched in the drawers for a pen or pencil, but met with disappointment.

'Can you get me a pencil?' she asked as she took the water from him. 'I'd—like to write you a note.' She watched his face, noticing the swift flash of eagerness that lit his eyes before it faded again.

'It would be wrong——' he began, but Lynn saw that he was already weakening.

'I need help, Conn!' There, it was out, and if he should report the matter to Rad then she would have to take the consequences. 'I was brought here against my will—but you know that. I want to get away——' She stopped as he shook his head. The next moment he was gone, having gestured abruptly, telling her to close the window.

Why was he so afraid of Rad? He had been almost ready to do her bidding and fetch a pencil for her, but without warning he had changed his mind, turning swiftly away. Lynn came to the conclusion that the money Rad was paying him was more important to Conn than his desire to help her. He was sitting on the step of an unoccupied caravan now—Olave's caravan, Lynn had decided, because no one had gone into it to her knowledge since Olave went away. She stood at the window staring out at him for a long while, but he was determined not to glance her way and at last she withdrew, sitting down on the couch, trying desperately to find a way of exploiting the situation. For she was sure that Conn could either be won over or, perhaps more likely, bought over. But she had no money here, having left it all in her handbag which was tucked away in the bottom of one of her suitcases in the boot of her car. She could make Conn a firm promise, though ... Lynn's scheming came to an abrupt end before it had got under way, simply because it would never work. Conn was not going to trust her to send on the money, and in any case, how would she know where to send it?

Yet if her plan was doomed to failure then why had she felt instinctively that Conn could—or would—help her?

'It's no use,' she whispered despairingly. 'I'm here until that fiend lets me go—and that won't be until he gets tired of me and wants a change.' Tired ... Even though she had slept with him for only one night Lynn was absolutely sure that she would be able to satisfy her husband's needs for a long time to come. He had derived the most supreme satisfaction and, to her surprise, had admitted this when, his ardour slowly cooling, he had put his arm across her body and told her she was 'divine'. He had seemed so blissfully happy and contented that Lynn had cried mentally in despair. If she gave him everything he desired of a woman then what chance had she of escaping from his clutches?

Where was he now? she wondered. He had been gone for several hours and Lynn could not imagine what he could be doing. Most gipsies were tinkers, of course—but nothing was less feasible to Lynn's mind than that her husband would travel the countryside going from door to door asking if there were any pans or kettles to mend! He was too proud, too arrogant by far, with a most inflated sense of his own superiority.

Another hour dragged by. Lynn had done all she could with the tiny kitchen, but had to admit that it looked little better for her efforts. The walls were faded, the floor covering of thin linoleum worn down in places to the canvas backing. She did manage to put a shine on a couple of pans, after finding some scouring powder at the back of a shelf containing a miscellany of articles ranging from some rusty razor-blades and a couple of mousetraps, to a jar of mouldy jam and a pair of moth-eaten woollen gloves.

After cleaning the pans she peeled and washed some vegetables which one of the gipsy women had brought to Rad just before he went out, along with two tins of stewed steak. Lynn put the vegetables in one pan and the meat in the other. She could not begin cooking anything until Rad returned.

She began pacing to and fro in the narrow space between the window and the alcove, feeling like a caged lion.

How long could this continue? She stopped in the

middle of the floor and burst into tears. Her nerves were shattered already and she did wonder if her mind would eventually be affected by this imprisonment. If only she had not struck Rad ... But as always she came back to the fact that he had deserved it and that it was only natural that her first impulse on seeing him again was to do something to pay him back.

He returned at last, and so overwrought had she become by her solitary confinement that she was actually glad to see him! Yet his first words, as his eyes scanned the caravan's newly-cleaned interior, set her teeth on edge and her temper soaring.

'So ... you decided to obey me. Wise girl!' His black eyes, transferred to her pallid face, took in the clear evidence of tears recently shed. 'Sorry for yourself, eh? You could be worse off. I could——'

'Worse off!' she flashed, uncaring if he should subject her to some violence. 'How, might I ask, could I be any worse off than I am now?'

For a moment he made no answer, but regarded her from his superior height with an expression of sardonic amusement.

'I could beat you every day,' he answered at last.

She coloured swiftly, and clenched her fists. And before she could stop herself she was saying, her voice rising in a crescendo of near-hysteria,

'That would at least relieve the monotony!'

Rad laughed, but it was a good-humoured laugh which brought a remarkable transformation to his features. She had owned already that he was handsome; when he laughed like this he was devastatingly attractive!

'Would you like me to oblige you, then?'

'I hate you,' said Lynn through her teeth. 'One day I might get the chance to lay you low——' She broke off as he laughed again. 'Or kill you!' she added on the high-pitched note she had used previously.

'I expect it would afford you extreme satisfaction to see me lying dead,' he remarked casually, walking into the kitchen to see what she had done there. 'Not bad, but I feel you could have done better. Sit down and tell me about yourself. What kind of work did you do? It was not domestic work, that's for sure,' he added, flicking a disparaging hand to indicate the walls she had not bothered to clean very much.

'I worked in an office.' Lynn glowered at him as he sat down on the couch. 'My employers will be making inquiries about me.'

'I mean to come to that in a few moments,' he returned cryptically. 'Meanwhile, tell me about yourself?'

She looked curiously at him; her temper had settled, much to her surprise. She felt calmer, not so highly-strung. She had to admit to herself that she was glad of someone to talk to, even though that someone was the man she hated with such intensity that she really did believe she could have struck him a mortal blow if that had been at all possible.

'I lived in a small apartment,' she began, moving over to a stool by the table and sitting down on it.

'Alone?' he queried, idly lifting a hand and examining his fingernails. She looked at them. They were immaculate, and yet he brought out a file and began to trim them with it. A gipsy attending to his fingernails! He glanced up, lifting one eyebrow inquiringly. She said tautly,

'Yes, I lived alone.' He knew she had no relatives, as he had asked her this previously. Reluctantly she had admitted that she had no one except a distant cousin whom she had not seen for over six years. She would have liked to have told him a lie, saying she had numerous relatives who would be inquiring about her, but she had always been incurably truthful and even in these circumstances she could not bring herself to look him in the face and tell an untruth. Besides, she had a shrewd suspicion that those piercing black eyes of his would have read her inner thoughts. She had friends, though, she had told him, and they would be wondering where she was. She reminded him about them now, but he shrugged this off and asked if she had a boy-friend. His eyes glinted as he added,

'You weren't engaged, were you?' He shook his head, and answered his own question. 'No, for if you were you wouldn't have been here on holiday alone.'

How stupid of her to tell him that! But as at the time she was almost out of her mind with terror, it was perhaps understandable that she should have revealed so much about herself.

'You say you worked in an office,' Rad was commenting. 'What did you do?'

Lynn told him, her attention suddenly caught by his clothes. The sweater he wore was not the one he had gone out in that morning! This one had slightly longer sleeves. His slacks had been pressed ... Lynn looked at his hair and felt convinced that it had been newly washed. Where had he spent the day? It would appear that he had some house—perhaps not too far from where she had met him in the woods—to which he could go. Should she ask him where he had been? On consideration she decided it would be a waste of time, sure that he would not tell her. He was speaking, saying her car should be arriving within the next hour or so.

'I might find it useful,' he added in some amusement.

'You ... thief! I suppose you stole that horse as well!'

His mouth went tight.

'Careful, wife,' he snapped. 'You do ask for it, don't you? Will you never learn that the wife of a gipsy treats her husband as her superior?'

Lynn's nerves tightened as her anger increased.

'I consider you and your kind as my *inferiors*! So get that!'

He rose, dropping the nail file into his pocket. His fingers gripped her wrist, jerking her to her feet. She came up in front of him; her head was savagely drawn back as he tugged at her hair, and she looked fearfully into his evil countenance. Even yet again she asked herself why she so continuously threw caution to the winds. She waited, nerves tensed, for whatever he intended doing to her as a punishment for this further insult. But to her surprise and relief she was given the chance of apologising, which she did, caution overcoming the impulse to tell him to go to the devil, that she was not apologising to a mere gipsy!

But she did not get away without any reprisal at all. On the contrary, the kiss he forced upon her was so ruthless and painful that tears were brought to her eyes. And when at last he withdrew she could only stare up at him through glistening eyelashes, her mouth quivering piteously, her high wide forehead puckered in a frown of protest.

For a long moment there was silence in the little caravan, a profound unfathomable silence that seemed to have emotional currents running through it. And then, with the most odd expression in his eyes, Rad bent his head again and kissed her so gently that a wave of of astonishment swept through her.

'Lynn ... why do you keep on asking for it?' he

murmured, and she knew instinctively that he meant that question to be for his own mind alone. He had not meant to speak the words aloud. Bewildered by the change in him, and with so many conflicting images darting about in her mind, she could only keep on staring, her lovely eyes wide, and moist with tears. His jaw was taut, but in his throat a muscle pulsated uncontrollably. 'Get my meal ready!' he snapped, breaking a spell which Lynn, to her amazement, wished to prolong.

Later, as they sat at the table, Rad referred to what she had said about her employers making inquiries about her.

'You'll write a letter telling them that you decided to get married——'

'Write——!' She gave him an astounded look. 'You believe you can smooth this over as simply as that!'

Her husband regarded her with a hint of impatience.

'Please try not to interrupt me, Lynn. If you write this letter your employers will accept your word, since there's no reason why they should not, is there?' He took up his fork, looked at it as if ascertaining whether or not it was clean, then picked up his knife. 'Any friends you have will be similarly notified of your marriage—— No, don't interrupt,' he warned imperiously as she again opened her mouth. 'You *will* write these letters, Lynn, even though at this moment you're determined not to.'

'You can't make me!' she cried, but the break in her voice spoke plainly of a lack of confidence. With a sinking heart she was resigned to obedience. If need be he would stand over her, most likely with that riding-crop with which he already threatened her.

And he did stand over her, having produced some high quality notepaper with matching envelopes. He had turned a section of the notepaper under, hiding an address, she knew. She asked him about it and was told that he would later cut the top off. Why, she wondered, hadn't he cut it off already?

'I stole the notepaper,' he said casually, and his hand came down, slapping hers hard as she defiantly tried to turn the paper over so that she could read the address.

She wrote as directed, crying softly all the time. These letters would be received with surprise, but as Rad had said, they would be taken as the truth, which they were, of course. She *was* married, and she *had* made her home in Southern Ireland.

Rad went out later, having sealed the envelopes while Lynn was in the kitchen washing the dishes. Had he gone to post them? She supposed there would be a post-box somewhere about.

Darkness came down and he had not returned. Lynn, startled by a furtive tap on the window, soon realised who it was and her heart gave a jerk. Conn!

He whispered to her as she opened the window.

'I've brought you a pencil, lady.'

'Thank you—oh, thank you very much! Come back when you can and I'll have a note for you.' She was trembling all over as she closed the window. The giving of the pencil was surely in itself the promise of help!

Rad came back carrying her two suitcases, which he laid, one on top of the other, on the couch. Then after lighting the lamp, he told her to open the top case.

'Why?' she wanted to know.

'I rather think you are the kind of girl who will have exceedingly pretty nightwear.' His voice was edged with satire; his black eyes looked mockingly into hers. She seethed. How she hated him! He spoke very softly. 'I said, open up the case.'

Lynn obeyed, colouring when she came to the diaphanous pearl-rose nightgown with its matching neg-ligé. Her husband spoke again in that same quiet tone of voice, telling her to take it out. She did—and threw it at him. With a laugh and an upraised hand he snatched it from mid-air.

'Thanks,' he said, 'I take it this is an invitation for me to dress you up in it?'

Her colour heightened, spreading right up to her hairline. Rad stood, holding the nightgown, laughing at her with his coal black eyes ... roguish eyes that held an expression that made her heart give a strange little jerk, the cause of which was neither revulsion nor fear. A tense moment ensued, as they stood there, staring at one another. Lynn, her mental visions expanding before her, stood naked in front of him as he slipped the nightgown over her head. She knew the touch of those long sensitive hands on her flesh, the nearness of his strong lithe body, the cool clean zephyr of his breath on her face as he bent his head to claim her lips.

'Give it back to me!' she demanded, furious at her thoughts. 'I won't wear it——'

'I think you will,' he broke in quietly, 'because it is my wish that you shall.' The material was soft and seductive to his fingers; Lynn knew that he was mentally stripping her, then seeing her clad in a way that every curve of her body was revealed to him. She turned away, was caught by his hand and brought round again. She felt his warmth as he unbuttoned her dress, stood impassive as he took it off. And soon she was having the nightgown slipped over her head, was caught up in his arms, knew the fierce passion of his kisses, and the full strength of his ardour...

CHAPTER FOUR

THE following day Lynn wanted to wash her hair. Rad had been out after breakfast and fetched some water in a large plastic container, and his casual remark when she told him about her hair was,

'Get on with it, then. There's plenty of water.'

She simmered with rage.

'Don't talk to me like that! Anyone would think I was your inferior!'

'And aren't you?' he queried softly.

'You obviously consider yourself as being above me,' she quivered. 'But our opinions differ. Who are you, anyway?' Her voice took on a curious note and her blue eyes were inquiring. 'Are you the king of the gipsies?'

For a moment she thought he did not intend to answer, but suddenly he threw back his curly head and laughed.

'That'll do very nicely! Yes, wife, I'm the king of the gipsies!'

She coloured at his sarcasm, and the mocking way in which he was regarding her. Hateful creature!

'Which obviously means that you are *not* the king of the gipsies,' she said stiffly. Her hand was automatically running through her soft dark hair and she frowned a little at the knowledge that it was becoming greasy.

Rad regarded her curiously from his seat on the couch.

'What made you think I might be?' he wanted to know.

She hesitated, loath to tell him that she had noticed a certain superiority about him. She merely said off-handedly,

'You're a little different from the rest around here.'

'A *little* different?' The inflection in his voice instantly brought to her mind a previous occasion when he had been *hurt* by something she had said. She gave him a look of incomprehension, quite unable to see why he should again be hurt.

And yet he was hurt. It was almost as if, although he was a gipsy, he had no desire at all to be recognised as one!

'That's what I said.' Lynn's words were forced out against reluctance, amazing her. She realised that she did not want to hurt this vagabond husband of hers!

He said quietly,

'How can you make a comparison? You haven't met any of the men in the camp.'

'I've seen them through the window, and heard them talking. You seem to forget that I've been here two days,' she just had to add, and an involuntary shudder passed through her. 'It seems like two years!' she flashed, and all her husband did was laugh. Had he forgotten his hurt already? Lynn was of the opinion that he could conceal his feelings without any trouble at all.

'What about your hair?' he asked, changing the subject. 'You'll have to boil some water on the stove.'

'I can't wash my hair in that absurdly small sink.' Unknowingly her eyes were appealing. Rad's expression changed and a slight frown knit his brow.

'What else can you do?' His glance went to her hair and the frown deepened. Was he really concerned? If so, his concern did not fit in with his first casual advice that she should 'get on with it'.

'If I had a large bowl...?'

'I'll see if I can get you one,' he promised, rising and moving towards the door. 'Have you a shampoo?'

'I think so—in one of my cases.' They were still at one end of the couch and Rad's eyes slid to them.

'Have a look and make sure. If you haven't I can possibly manage to get you one.'

Lynn was a little taken aback.

'Do your people use such luxuries as shampoos?' she asked.

'My people...' with a sudden incomprehensible frown. 'The gipsies do sometimes have shampoos; people give them all kinds of things.'

'In order not to be cursed, I expect!' This came out before Lynn could stop it, as she remembered how a school friend's mother had been so scared of being cursed by a gipsy that she showered small gifts upon her every time she called at the house.

Rad, surprisingly unruffled by what she had said, threw her a look of amusement and asked,

'Do you really believe that gipsies can put a curse on you?'

'No,' she answered, shaking her head, 'I personally don't, but I've known someone whose fear of being cursed was very great indeed.' Rad was still by the door, his hand on the knob; he told her again to look for the shampoo.

'I'm almost sure I have one...' She took several articles from the top suitcase, including a leather shoulder-bag which came open as she made to lay it on a stool. Something dropped from it and Rad, stooping, picked it up. A very strange expression came over his swarthy face as he looked down at the front page of the little booklet. Lynn, the shoulder-bag still in her hand, could only stare at him uncomprehendingly, trying to read what lay behind those piercing black eyes of his.

'How did you come by this?' he asked at length, lifting his gaze from the booklet to look into her face.

'It's from someone's stately home,' she replied. 'Ballytara Abbey; I visited it the other day.' Was it only the other day? It seemed a century since she had roamed so freely in the sunlit gardens of the mansion which, the farmer's wife had said, belonged to a gentleman by the name of Mr de Gais, a gentleman who was obviously descended from a titled family, since it was a Viscountess de Gais who had designed the formal terraces to the south front of the house. 'The gardens are thrown open on certain days during the summer,' she went on, noticing that her husband was expecting her to say more about her visit. 'The gardens are beautiful. The owner of Ballytara Abbey must be a millionaire, I should think.' Her voice was dreamy, her hyacinth-blue eyes pensive. How she wished she were there now, free! *Free!* Her lip quivered as the pleasant memory stayed with her, torturing her as it reminded her of her imprisonment. She said, murmuring softly to herself, 'I was so happy then...' A tiny sob escaped her, but she could not move, or turn away from the curious scrutiny with which her husband was regarding her.

'Did you enjoy your visit so very much, then?' And, before she could answer, 'When were you there?' Such a puzzling inflection in his voice now. It might almost have been of considerable importance to him to know when she had been to the gardens of Ballytara Abbey.

'Last Saturday.' She was looking up, right into his eyes and all unconscious that her own eyes were appealing, just as they had been a few minutes ago. The shoulder-bag, clasped tightly in her hands, was still open, but she made no attempt to close it. Vaguely she knew that her purse was in it ... and a good deal of money ... enough, perhaps, to bribe the young man, Conn.

'Last Saturday...' He became reflective, as if he were attempting to recall his own movements of that day. Driven by some force she could not understand, she found herself helping him by saying,

'The afternoon before you abducted me.'

He nodded, still thoughtful.

'Tell me, what did you think about the gardens?'

She stared blankly at him for a moment before asking,

'Have you been there?'

Silence, deep and profound. Was it a hint of amusement that lifted one corner of that firm implacable mouth?

'Yes, as a matter of fact I have.'

Lynn frowned.

'They let you in——?' She stopped, heart jerking. Once again she had said the wrong thing. His black eyes blazed with fury. Oh, but there was no doubt that he was a wild, uncivilised gipsy, whether he liked the idea or not!

'Explain!' he commanded, coming menacingly close to her. 'Can it be that you think me unfit to mix with the people who go there, to enjoy the gardens?'

'I'm sorry,' she rejoined meekly. 'I suppose I felt that—that——'

'Yes, you felt—what?'

Lynn spread her hands helplessly.

'I'm sorry,' she said again. 'Please forget it.'

Another silence followed her words and for a while she waited breathlessly for some kind of reprisal. Let him shake her! She was past caring what he did to her. She was his prisoner, totally in his power, under his primitive domination. Why allow fear to hold her like this? Far easier and less wearing to accept with resignation whatever chastisements he might think fit to mete out to her.

However, he merely gave her back the little booklet, flicking a hand towards the open suitcase.

'The shampoo,' he said curtly. 'See if you have it.'

Lynn watched from the window as he walked away from the caravan after she had assured him she had the shampoo. How arresting was his tall lean figure! There was a sort of majestic rhythm about his way of striding out. She wondered why she had not noticed things like this on that other occasion. Yet, as she had already told herself, it was not to be expected that she would be aware of anything other than her own desperate plight and the danger of her position. Her mind went to the girl who had saved her, a girl who was obviously an important person in Rad's life at that particular time, for she had him obeying her only seconds after telling him to leave Lynn alone.

Obeying her ... A frown creased Lynn's forehead. Rad meekly obeying a gipsy girl? It was incredible, and if Lynn had not witnessed the scene herself she would never have believed it. Had the girl some hold over him that she could command and he obey? Yet if she did have some hold on him he would not have dared leave her and marry someone else. Should she ask him about the girl? It would be interesting to watch his reaction, to discover what explanation there had been for his swift subjugation to her will. But after some contemplation of the matter Lynn decided not to risk her husband's anger by bringing up that first encounter. He himself had never once referred to it and she felt sure that he was ashamed of his conduct—perhaps not greatly so, but certainly enough for him to want to forget it.

He returned, carrying a large plastic bowl of a bright yellow colour.

'Will this do?' he asked, and she nodded.

'It amazes me that you'll trouble yourself,' she could not resist saying as she took the bowl from his hand.

'I do have my moments,' he returned with a hint of amusement. 'I said you hadn't seen the worst of me, but neither have you seen the best of me.' So curious his voice, so unfathomable his expression. Lynn, holding the bright yellow bowl against her, knew a sudden urge to learn more about her husband, to discover what was the best of him.

She shrugged, though, and turned abruptly away. She really had nothing in her mind which was so strong as the desire to escape, so why bother to dwell on the more attractive traits which this husband of hers might possess?

She washed her hair, then came into the living part of the caravan, holding a towel. To her surprise Rad got up from the couch where he had been idly reading a magazine, took the towel from her hands, and began rubbing her hair vigorously. His body was close and she could actually feel its warmth; his touch was oddly gentle when at length he threw aside the towel and cupped her face between his smooth-palmed hands, tilting her head and staring down with a sort of brooding expression into her beautiful blue eyes. Her mouth quivered convulsively, because she had been thinking about the pleasant visits to the hairdressers, when she had chatted with the girl who ran the salon, Jean, who had become a friend of hers. Lynn was almost crying now, wondering if she would ever visit a hairdressing salon again, wondering if she would ever be able to look back on this desperate situation she was in and say,

'Thank God I escaped!'

Rad's voice drifted into her thoughts, a soft voice and gentle in its intonation.

'How beautiful you are, my Lynn!' His mouth claimed hers and she made no resistance. He frowned a little and told her to reciprocate.

She obeyed, then unexpectedly dissolved into tears.

'I—I—— Oh, please let me go!' she almost shouted. 'I can't stand it much longer!'

'My kisses?' he wanted to know.

'Everything! Don't you see that I can't face being a prisoner all my life!' She twisted from him and stood facing him, hands behind her back, resting on a rickety shelf. Her hair looked wild about her face and shoulders, her cheeks were white, her eyes filled with tears. 'Let me go?' she pleaded, becoming immeasurably humble in her attempt to soften him. 'You can't keep me in this tiny caravan indefinitely—it isn't possible. You know it isn't.'

The black eyes seemed to shadow as the lazy lids drooped a little. Had she touched some hidden chord of humanity that he might possess? After all, he had said she hadn't seen the best of him, so there might be some tiny measure of compassion in his make-up. But to her utter despair he was shaking his head and saying, an inflexibility in his voice that could not possibly be ignored,

'My wife stays with me, Lynn. You married me willingly——'

'Willingly!' she gasped. 'Oh, how can you say such a thing!'

'You made no protest when the ceremony was being performed,' was Rad's smooth reminder, and Lynn's eyes became downcast. 'Ah, I see,' her husband murmured perceptively. 'You had hopes of escape once you were outside this caravan, did you?'

'Could you blame me?' she queried fractiously. 'Of course I had hopes of escape.'

'And you probably still have hopes?'

She thought of Conn, who had brought her the pencil so that she could send him a note. She thought of the money in her purse ... and decided with a sort of panic that she must hide it from her husband just as soon as the opportunity arose.

'I shall always be on the alert,' she admitted frankly. 'No one in my position would become resigned.'

'No, I suppose not,' he agreed reasonably, and then he became thoughtful, his dark eyes wandering to the booklet which now lay on the far end of the shelf by which his wife was standing. He sighed, deeply, and she shot him a bewildered look. There was something ... something most peculiar about him, and about this whole business altogether. She thought again of Conn, and hoped she could get some information out of him—though what kind of information she was seeking was by no means clear in her mind.

Rad was coming to her; she stood still when he took hold of her. He seemed to be anxious to calm her, to see those tears go from her eyes.

'Please——' she began as he bent to kiss her. Of course, he took no notice, and again his kiss was gentle on her lips. He had to tell her once more to respond.

'No, I won't! I never will again!'

He sighed, surprising her, as she fully expected some savage reprisal, some brute endeavour to show her who was master.

'Brush your hair,' he advised, glancing at it with distaste. 'It won't look right if it dries like that.'

How did he know about a woman's hair? Lynn was sure the gipsy women had no pride in their appearances. Their hair was seldom washed, from what Lynn had seen, and she was almost sure that it often went without a brushing from one week to the next. Rad seemed to know far more than seemed possible, living as he did as a member of a tribe of nomads who, happy enough in their freedom, cared little or nothing for what went on in the civilised world outside their own insular environment, a world so very close, and yet so far away.

She had her brush and comb now and she used them, aware that her husband watched her every move with interest. What was he thinking as he sat there, his eyes moving now and then, from her face to her lovely slender body and back again? She noted his every feature—the lean and aquiline face with its sensuous mouth and outthrust chin, the straight black brows above rather lazy lids, the long eyelashes framing those black coals of fire. Her glance took in his hair; thick and wiry, it seemed to accentuate the effect of lawlessness. And yet she had to own that it was most attractive, curling the way it did.

Suddenly she was conscious of some strange mist of memory playing havoc with her mind as it endeavoured to penetrate through to her consciousness. She found herself searching ... for what? Again she examined her husband's face, looking at his mouth and remembering how his kisses were different on that first occasion, when he had assaulted her ... different in some way that was not quite definable. All she knew was that at first they were totally insulting, whereas now—although they were passionate and often merciless—they were never totally without respect. She looked for the nobility which was firmly stamped on Rad's face and recalled that it had not been manifest at first. But even yet again she was forced to find the explanation in the fact that she had been almost paralysed with fear, scarcely believing her luck when, with the appearance of the gipsy girl, she had escaped any further attack.

'What are you thinking?' Rad's voice, quiet and yet masterfully insistent, broke into her reflections. 'You appear—judging by your expression—to have a problem?'

'Yes,' she retorted instantly, 'the problem of my escape!'

'Which will never come to pass,' was her husband's cool assertion. 'You have another problem. What is it?'

Should she tell him of her bewilderment? If she did it would entail bringing up that other encounter, and as she had already decided against such folly, she merely shrugged and resumed brushing her hair. He repeated his question, this time in an even firmer tone of voice than that which he had just used.

Lynn twisted around again.

'I suppose I have to answer you?' She still disliked the idea of introducing the incident which would surely arouse his fury, but with this masterful look on his face and the unmistakable authority in his voice she was becoming resigned.

'Obviously. Why otherwise would I have asked it?'

'I might not answer truthfully.' She looked across at him, the hairbrush idle in her hand.

'I shall know if you lie to me.'

She thought of the gipsies who came round to the door, declaring they could tell fortunes. Did they really have second sight—some sixth sense acquired owing to their particular way of life?

'I was thinking of the first time you and I met.' There, it was out! Lynn mused on the fact that although she was really referring to the second meeting, the comparatively minor incident of the car was so overshadowed by it that always in her mind she regarded the second meeting as the first. She looked at Rad, saw his nostrils flare and knew a deep resentment that he should be angry, since it was she who was the injured party.

'You would be better forgetting that first meeting,' he advised, and Lynn saw that he too was attaching no importance to the incident of the car.

'Oh, and why?' she challenged, feeling that, having come so far, she might as well go the whole way.

'Because *I* am trying to forget it. The longer you keep it in mind the worse it will be for you.'

'I don't think I understand?' she returned, frowning in puzzlement.

'We'll not talk about it, Lynn.' Imperious the tone. Anyone would think he was far above her, to hear him speak in that superior manner!

'You're ashamed, that's why you want to forget!'

'*I'm* ashamed?' with a lift of his brows. '*You're* the one who ought to be ashamed!' Automatically he lifted a finger to the livid weal upon his cheek. 'We shall not talk about it—ever again!'

'But——'

'That's enough,' he snapped, glowering at her. 'Don't argue with me!'

Lynn resumed her hair brushing, puzzled by Rad's attitude. It was as though he was now so ashamed of that attack that he had no wish to be reminded of it. But why he should say that it was she herself who ought to be ashamed was something for which she could find no explanation, no matter how hard she tried. She shrugged at last, dismissing the matter. It was of no consequence anyway.

'I could do with a hair dryer,' she said after a while. 'But there's no electricity, is there?'

'We sometimes make our own.' He looked at her hair, and then at the window. 'We can go out into the sunshine if you like. It should dry quickly then.'

Lynn's eyes brightened.

'I'd like to go out,' she said.

He rose from the couch and stretched his long legs. He invariably wore an air of boredom, and Lynn wondered how a man of such physical vigour could spend his days in idleness.

They walked into the woods, Lynn conscious of the interest of the other gipsies. She had refused to have anything to do with them, and this seemed—strangely—to meet with her husband's full approval.

'There isn't much sun penetrating here,' she complained after a while. 'Can't we go along the road?'

Rad's lips twisted in a smile of sardonic amusement.

'No, my dear,' he said, 'we can't go along the road.'

'Afraid I'd try to escape?'

'I suspect you'd make some sort of an attempt.'

'Correct, I would.'

'You're honest if nothing else,' commented Rad.

'What exactly do you mean by the "nothing else"?' she wanted to know.

'Your arrogance, your inflated ego that causes you to despise other people——'

'*My* arrogance!' she could not help interrupting. 'What about yours?'

'If I am arrogant with you, Lynn, then it's because you have asked for it.' His voice was soft yet admonishing, making Lynn feel like a naughty child who was having a well-deserved telling off. It was a most unpleasant sensation and one which, naturally, aroused her temper. However, this was one of the few instances when her prudence overcame her temerity and she said nothing, merely allowing her temper to simmer inside her. And as Rad seemed not to be in a talkative frame of mind they strolled along in silence for some considerable time. She stole a glance now and then at his stern set profile and as always was struck by the nobility, the air of the aristocrat—this despite the way he dressed, which proclaimed him a gipsy born and bred, especially with his hair wild like this, blown as it was by the breeze coming over the hills in the distance.

They were out for half an hour, Rad having chosen a lonely dell where he obviously felt secure against the possibility of meeting anyone else. Lynn, after looking all around, prayed the whole time that she would espy someone, if only a solitary rambler. But obviously Rad knew what he was about, and wouldn't have brought her if there had been any risk involved.

'Your hair's dry now?' he said when they were back in the caravan. He took a handful and allowed it to flow through his fingers. 'It's very beautiful.' He brought it to his face. Lynn snatched herself away, telling him to leave her alone. Within seconds she was regretting her folly. Crushed to his hard frame, her mouth bruised by the ruthlessness of his, she wished with all her heart she could control her anger, as she always suffered when it flared out at him.

'One of these days you'll find yourself nursing a few bruises,' he warned when presently he held her at arms' length. 'The sooner you accept me as your master the more pleasant your life will be.'

'Pleasant? Do you suppose life with you will ever be pleasant?'

'I believe it could be much pleasanter than it is.'

'You amaze me!'

'I believe I am talking some sense,' he said, walking to the window and standing there, looking out on to the other caravans. Did he really care whether or not her life became more pleasant? Lynn certainly did not want *his* life to become more pleasant. Just the reverse. She desired only that he'd come to regret his hasty marriage, and let her go.

Turning at last, he spoke softly to her, ordering her to get a meal ready. For a long defiant moment she stood unmoving, seething with anger at being treated like a servant.

'I hope, Lynn,' he said, 'that I won't have to ask you twice.'

She swung away, through the alcove. Tears were in her eyes when eventually she returned with a plate of bacon, eggs and sausage—luxuries which Rad had brought in with him yesterday, and which, she surmised, he had stolen from somewhere. Perhaps he shoplifted in one of the supermarkets. The idea brought a deep frown to her forehead and this, along with her tears, caused her husband to snap impatiently,

'What the devil's wrong with you now? An irascible, scowling woman is not for me! Put a more pleasant look on your face or I'll give you something to cry for!' Although it was anger which edged his voice Lynn was alert to another inflection altogether. Rad seemed tired, dejected even, and it occurred to her that the necessity of keeping so close a watch on her might already have become irksome to him. However, she wisely held her tongue and after a moment he asked her where her own meal was.

'I'm not hungry,' she replied.

'Nevertheless, you will please me by eating something.' So aloof and dignified! He might have been a king, she thought, or at least a nobleman with a proud family lineage.

'Even you can't force me to eat,' she said in cold

emphatic tones. 'I don't want anything, and that's the end of it.'

But of course it was not the end of it. She was ordered to cook more food and this she did, too dispirited to continue an argument which she knew full well she could not win.

'I see you are learning,' he said in a tone she was bound to detest.

'I hope,' she said bitterly, 'that your domination affords you satisfaction!'

'It does,' was his calm rejoinder. 'Anything which brings you humiliation is satisfying to me. It will be a long time yet before your punishment comes to an end.'

'Comes to an end?' she cried, seizing on this. 'It *will* come to an end some time, then?'

'I don't envisage spreading my revenge over the next forty or fifty years,' he said with a dash of amusement in his tone.

She shivered visibly and said, in a low and hollow voice,

'I hope I die long before then.'

The black eyes seemed to take on a startled look.

'Life for a child like you should be sweet.'

'Don't talk like a fool!' she flashed, throwing all caution to the winds. 'My life is hell, and you know it!'

'At present, yes,' he agreed, but cryptically.

'There's no future for me if you don't let me go.'

His mouth tightened.

'Let's change the subject, Lynn. Tell me some more about yourself. Do you realise that I don't even know your age?'

She told him; he then asked if she had any idea of his own age. She studied him, as she had studied him so many times before. Already she had estimated his age to be around thirty, even though he did appear to be a few years older.

He smiled when she spoke and said yes, he was thirty last birthday.

'What else must I know about you?' he went on. 'Just talk, Lynn; I like to hear you talk.'

She glanced at him, her surprise plain for him to see.

'Not always,' she said. 'You can't.'

He inclined his head in agreement.

'Not when you choose to act like a termagant—which, unfortunately, is often. You have a charming voice, my dear, and it's a pity to spoil it the way you do.'

Lynn sent him a speaking glance, yet for some inconceivable reason she had no counter-thrust ready. She ate a little of her food, then talked as he had bidden her to, and he listened with deep interest, so that when at length she had finished speaking there was little about her life that was hidden from him.

'This Thomas,' he said, 'he sounds as dull as can be.'

'Did I make him sound dull?'

'Very dull.' Rad toyed with a bread roll and Lynn looked at his hands, noting again how well kept they were.

'I didn't mean to make him dull,' she said.

'He wasn't the man for you. Although you'll hotly deny it, you need excitement.'

'No such thing!' retorted Lynn indignantly.

'I said you'd deny it.' Rad's mouth twitched a little. 'You're very transparent, Lynn.' He paused a moment, expecting her to speak, but she was busy with her food, having discovered that she *was* rather hungry, after all.

'It's a pity you have this superiority complex,' he went on. 'It's time you learned that people are people, and that only criminals are to be despised, and not those who, by an accident of birth, happen to be different from you.' His voice, finely-timbred so as to be most attractive, had, for the very first time, an almost imperceptible suggestion of a soft Irish burr. Had he been deliberately adopting another form of speech, and now for a moment been off his guard? He certainly had a very different intonation from the other gipsies she had heard, though quite often his voice would be edged with that roughness which characterised the voices of the other men, including Olave and Conn—this when he was in one of his furies. He was looking at her censoriously, and yet with a sort of regret in his eyes. Lynn sighed, half wishing she could understand him but at the same time telling herself she was too indifferent to bother trying to understand him. What good would it do her anyway?

'I've never before been accused of having a superiority complex,' she just had to say in her defence.

'But you have one where I am concerned?'

'Because you're beyond the pale.'

An awful silence followed, with the icy chill of her husband's wrath seeming to pervade the whole caravan.

'If you're not careful,' he told her harshly, 'you'll be black and blue!'

Swallowing convulsively, Lynn averted her head, quite unable to meet the threat in her husband's eyes.

For the rest of the meal no word was said between them, and when it was over Rad went out, asking her first if she wanted the lamp lighting.

She shook her head, depressed because he was leaving her. It was not that she really wanted his company, but it was preferable to hours of solitary confinement where she had nothing to do except sit on the couch and wallow in her misery.

'It isn't dark yet.'

'It will be soon.'

'Then I'll go to bed.' Bed! How she hated the thought of sleeping with anyone so low and uncivilised as a gipsy!

'I'll put it down for you,' he offered, and she watched with a rising hatred of him as he brought it from its place in the wall.

When he had gone she took out her purse and hid it behind some tins in the cupboard under the sink. Then she cleared away the dishes and washed them up.

'And now for that note,' she said, taking out a writing-pad from her case. She had her own pen and pencil now, but she used the pencil given her by Conn.

It was a difficult note to write, but eventually she managed it, conveying to Conn that she would reward him immediately, but that she would also send him some more money on when she arrived home. He would of course have to provide her with an address. The reward she offered added up to just about the whole of her savings, but that did not trouble her in the least. She had to make the payment such that Conn would not be able to resist taking a chance and helping her to escape. What form that escape would take Lynn could not visualise, but she hoped that if her husband went off for the whole day again Conn might be able to get her away from the camp without her being seen by any of the others.

With the note written she sat down, to brood again, passing away the lonely hours and wondering how any girl, in these days, could find herself in a position like this.

CHAPTER FIVE

Darkness had fallen and still Lynn sat there, in the tiny caravan, alone and thinking of her home in England, of her friends and her comfortable job in the office of a firm of agricultural engineers. A fire had been lighted outside and she could hear the chatter and laughter of gipsies as they gathered around it. Lynn, nerves tensed and her mind sunk in the deepest dejection, felt that her senses must surely be affected if this went on much longer. What good would she be to Rad then? If he had any idea just how she felt then surely he must see that he would be the loser in the end.

Suddenly she sat up, her ears alert. A gentle tap on the window brought her springing to her feet. Earlier she had drawn the curtains; now she cautiously pulled one back.

'Conn!'

'Hush,' he whispered as she opened the window a little. 'Don't make such a noise.'

'I can't help it,' she whispered, her heart thumping so hard that she actually felt a physical pain. 'It squeaks when I pull it towards me.'

'Have you the note?'

She fetched it at once and handed it to him.

'Be careful, Conn. Don't let anyone see you.'

'I must go,' he whispered. 'Goodnight, lady.'

'Goodnight, Conn—and thank you so very much.'

'I don't know if I can help you,' he said, and the next moment he was gone, fading into the darkness.

At the other end of the caravan the firelight shone on the curtains, lighting their drab colour with a crimson glow. No one would have noticed Conn, in the darkness at the other end of the caravan, she thought, and yet her heart was still beating far too quickly and for a long moment she could not move, as she waited, fear catching at her throat, to see if her husband had, by some perverse working of fate, happened to see what had occurred. But all was well, and when Rad came in about half an hour later there was nothing in his face to denote that he had any inkling of what was going on.

He lighted the lamp immediately, asking a little harshly why she was sitting in the dark.

'Making a martyr of yourself?' he added before she could speak.

'Why should you care?' she snapped.

'I don't.' He glanced around. 'What have you been doing?'

'Nothing!'

He turned abruptly and went into the tiny kitchen.

'Do you want a drink of anything?' he asked.

'No, I don't.'

'Have you had one?'

'No.'

Exasperatedly he sighed; she heard him angrily rattling a cup and saucer and wondered why he had not ordered her to make the drink for him.

He came back in about five minutes carrying a cup of cocoa. She asked pettishly,

'Where have you been?'

To her surprise he took this with nothing more alarming than a mild stare and she found herself absurdly disappointed, aware that she wanted to quarrel with him. Of course, she had only to call him an uncouth gipsy ne'er-do-well and she would very soon have a quarrel on her hands.

Ignoring her question as if it were beneath his dignity to answer it, Rad sat down on a stool, his eyes trained upon her.

'Tomorrow,' he said, 'I shall expect to see you dressed in something different.'

Lynn's eyes flashed fire, revealing the fury that had been smouldering all evening.

'I shall wear what I like!'

'I believe you're deliberately making yourself look drab. It won't do, Lynn. I want to see you wearing some of the pretty clothes you must have brought with you on this holiday you were having.'

Her glance strayed to the suitcases, still not unpacked, as she could not bear to put her clothes in the rickety cupboard which, she surmised, served both as a clothes cupboard and a receptacle for everything that had no proper place. That this was not Rad's caravan she had soon decided, since there was scarcely anything of his in it. She had pondered on where his belongings could be, but had given up, resigned to the fact that she would never know much about her husband anyway. He was a secretive man who seemed often to be preoccupied with that deep concentration Lynn had often seen on the faces of businessmen who used to come into the office, a concentration not at all in keeping with the life he led as a gipsy whose time was spent entirely in idleness.

'I fail to see the sense of wearing nice clothes when I'm not going anywhere,' she said, watching her husband as he sipped the hot chocolate.

He hesitated a moment and then,

'Tomorrow you and I will be on the move. We'll travel in your car. We shall be staying the night at another camp.'

Her heart seemed as if it would stop beating, and

only now did she fully realise just how much faith she had put in Conn and the possibility of his helping her to escape.

'The rest of the camp are not moving?'

'No, just you and I.'

Without knowing it Lynn wrung her hands.

'I don't want to move from here...' She tailed off, aware of her stupidity. Rad was examining her face intently over the rim of his cup.

'And why, might I ask, do you not want to move from here? From the moment you came you've been making complaints about the boredom.'

Lynn bit her lip, unable to find an answer, and as the moments went by the atmosphere seemed to be charged with tension. She managed to say at last,

'Here is as good as anywhere else. I don't feel up to roaming the countryside like—like the riff-raff gipsies.' She cared nothing for the drifts of crimson that crept up beneath her husband's dark skin. Her mind was solely on Conn, and the lost opportunity of making an early escape. Nothing mattered any more, now that the tiny spark of hope had been extinguished by Rad's decision to move, and she waited for the retaliation which she was certain would come her way. Strangely, though, Rad was suppressing the anger which she had deliberately tried to arouse.

'Perhaps, as you say, here is as good as anywhere else, but it so happens that I have to move.'

Lynn said curiously, putting aside her disappointment for a space,

'You *have* to move?'

'That's right—I have to move on to another camp.'

'And at this camp there will be a caravan for you?'

A sardonic twist to his lips was the prelude to the edge of mockery contained in his voice as he said,

'There will be a caravan for *us*.'

Rising from the couch, Lynn paced the floor, her small fists tightly clenched at her sides. Another camp, another caravan. More swarthy-skinned gipsies looking at her with that amused and curious expression in their dark eyes. More imprisonment, with a jailer there whenever her husband left the caravan.

'I can't stand much more of this!' she cried at last, her control breaking despite her efforts to keep a rein upon it. 'The inactivity's terrible! How any of you people can live in perpetual idleness is quite beyond my comprehension. Don't you ever get heartily sick of the boredom?'

Rad's eyelids came down and his mouth relaxed. He placed his cup and saucer on the table and rose from the stool, his face an expressionless mask. Tension was in the air again and a strange sort of puzzlement took everything else from Lynn's mind. Without trying to stem the impulse she spoke her thoughts aloud,

'There's a mystery about you. What do you do when you go out? I don't think you stay on the camp.'

To her amazement he turned abruptly from her searching gaze, turned in order to hide his expression completely. She spoke again, rapidly and in the sort of imperious tone of voice that was more characteristic of her husband than herself.

'I want to know! You're always reminding me that I'm your wife, so in that case I have a right to know how you spend your time. Tell me, I say!' Why she should be so vehement, why it seemed so vitally important that she learn more about this gipsy husband of hers, she could not explain. All she did know was that it had become a most pressing matter that she *should* discover more about him.

But to her chagrin and frustration he merely said, throwing the words over his shoulder,

'You have never considered yourself as my wife. When you do, and when you put yourself on my level, then you shall learn all there is to learn about me.'

On his level ... Lynn stared at his back, at his square aristocratic shoulders, his slim body which, despite his life of idleness, carried not an ounce of excess weight. In fact, everything about him was arresting—his figure, his looks, and the confident air with which he carried himself. Not for the first time Lynn found herself saying,

'If I didn't *know* he was a gipsy, I wouldn't believe he was one.' Inevitably her thoughts went to Olave, and the conversation she had overheard between him and Rad. Olave had mentioned the word 'position' which had stamped itself on Lynn's mind at the time, causing her to speculate on the possibility of Rad's being the king of the gipsies. She now knew he was not the king.

He brought himself round at last, and there did seem to be the mark of deep bitterness on his face. His eyes bored into her and she realised he wanted some comment in response to his assertion of a moment ago.

'I shall never consider myself as your equal.' Although there was an emphasis to these words Lynn spoke them quietly, for some reason not now desirous of causing any undue dissension between her husband and herself. She did not question this, but if she had she would probably have put it down to caution, since, in the next half hour or so, she would be lying in that bed with him, totally at his mercy.

'In that case,' returned Rad, 'you will never know any more about me than you do now.' It was a cold, harsh countenance which she saw, and all at once she had so strong a feeling of inferiority that she almost wanted to hang her head. Anger surged within her as a result and she would dearly have loved to hit back at him for this arrogant, superior attitude he was adopting. She repressed her inclination, however, and asked instead,

'Where are we going? I mean, where is this other camp you speak of?'

'Some great distance from here,' was all he would say.

'Your horse ... what will you do with it?' She knew that Olave was back, but she had not seen the horse on any of the occasions when she had taken a look through one or other of the windows. 'If you're going to use my car you can't be taking it with you.'

Rad said quietly, his manner unexpectedly tinged with satire,

'Seeing that I stole it, it shall be returned to its owner.'

Lynn coloured, and her blue eyes flashed.

'There's no need for sarcasm!'

'You did assert that I had stolen it, Lynn.'

'Why can't you tell me where you got it? After all, I think you'll agree that it isn't the kind of animal anyone would expect *you* to have.' She was regarding him curiously, sensing a mystery more acutely than ever. It seemed that with every minute that passed the man was becoming more and more of an enigma to her.

'One day,' he said between his teeth, 'you'll make one disparaging remark too many!' His tone was a mingling of rage and rancour. Plainly he was mortified by her repeated insults. To her own utter amazement Lynn found herself apologising.

'I'm sorry,' she said, and then, with the merest hint of persuasion, 'Won't you tell me how you came by such a beautiful animal? It's a thoroughbred, that's obvious.'

'How do you know so much about horses?'

'I don't know very much at all; but I used to ride—a few years ago—and several wealthy people in the area where the riding-school was situated owned horses like the one you have.' She stared at him, noticed his expression and resigned herself to disappointment. Rad would never tell her where he had obtained that horse. And she was right; he took up the cup and saucer, carried it into the kitchen, then began to take off his sweater.

'It's time we turned in,' he told her curtly. 'We've to be up early in the morning.'

She went hot, as she always did when she had to undress before him. But it was better to do it now, while he was similarly occupied, than to wait until he was in bed, half propped up, his dark eyes amorously roving her body, his mind exulting over the fact that it was his, to use as he wished.

Lynn was unbuttoning her blouse when he spoke again of the clothes she had in the suitcases. After making her bring some of them out he chose a dress of bright primrose cotton with a border of white daisies round the hem. The neckline was low-cut, and it was sleeveless—a sun-dress, in fact.

'You'll wear that,' he decided. 'Put it over the back of the couch.'

A sort of black rage filled her and instead of obeying him she threw the dress on the floor and stamped on it. Rad, after a little start of incredulity, did no more than to seize her by the waist, force her round to face him and, bending down, slap her hard and long on the thigh. She struggled and wept, but nothing was effective until his fury had exhausted itself, by which time

Lynn was sobbing piteously, her heartbeats wildly out of control.

'Pick it up!' he ordered, pointing to the dress. Lynn did as she was told, but unconsciously held the dress to her eyes and wept into it.

'I can't go on!' she cried, her voice muffled, and caught by her sobs. 'I *won't* go on—I'll—I'll k-kill myself!'

A tense little silence followed this threat before Rad, with a staggering transformation in his manner, took the dress from her clutching fingers, laid it aside, then gently brought his wife to him, holding her almost tenderly and speaking soothingly to her as he stroked her hair, having first taken it back from her face.

'My child ... why do you enrage me so?' His voice was not quite steady, his hand warm and caressing as it moved from her hair to her damp, burning cheek. 'If only you had some sense...' His voice trailed away and he seemed to flinch as her body jerked spasmodically in his arms, racked as it was by her sobs. 'When you're dealing with a gipsy you should take more care.' He murmured something else she could not hear properly but which sounded very much like, '... the brutal part of me...'

Lynn, craving for comfort as she was, clung to her husband, resting her face against his bare chest. She could hear his heart beating, was aware that her own heartbeats were slowly resuming their normal rhythm, that her sobs were diminishing in intensity. There was a peace and tranquillity in his tenderness, a soothing balm in the touch of his hands, the feel of his body so close to hers. She closed her eyes as one last lingering sigh brought an end to her sobs, and heard her husband say softly,

'That's better, my Lynn. Oh, but you must never cry like that again.'

At last she drew away, staring up at him through lashes still wet with tears. One hand was around her, the palm of the other on the nape of her neck, the fingers in her hair.

'You're—different,' she murmured, accepting the staggering truth that she wanted only to remain like this for a long time, savouring the comfort which, incredibly, her husband could give her. 'If y-you were—were always l-like this...' What was she saying—or trying to say? How could she be so content to be here, so close to the strong hard body that had inflicted such pain and insults on her own? Why did she not shrink from the touch of his hand, the unexpected caress of his lips as he bent his head and gently touched her mouth with his? 'Why—why are you different?'

To her surprise he shook his head, and those black eyes seemed to become dulled by regret.

'I can't explain,' he told her huskily. 'No, my child, I can't explain.' He drew away; she missed the quiet calm and contentment which his nearness had imparted to her. 'Come, child, it's time we slept ...' And with gentle hands he finished unbuttoning her blouse and took it off. 'Where is your nightdress?' he asked, and when she told him he brought it to her, then left her, going into the kitchen, and murmuring something about cleaning his teeth.

When he returned Lynn was standing in the nightgown, a rather pathetic figure, still smarting from the pain he had inflicted, yet bewildered by the incredible change which her threat had brought about in him. And now, as he stood there looking at her, she saw the slow pulsation of a muscle in his neck, noticed the slight movement in his chest with its mass of jet black hair. His arms too were covered with hair, though not very thickly. How very masculine he looked, with those wide shoulders, that slim body, that swarthy skin.

She watched his eyes move and knew he was looking through the diaphanous material of the nightgown to the vivid red marks he had made on her thigh. Embarrassed and humiliated, she averted her head, her mouth quivering convulsively. Rad came to her, lifted her face, and slowly shook his head. That he regretted his action she was sure ... just as she regretted her own violence—though his was not for the same reason. She strongly suspected that he hated himself for his lack of restraint, whereas her own regrets were owing to the reprisals which her act had brought down upon her head.

Lynn slept within his arms, her head resting against his breast; she still savoured the comfort he gave her and for the first time there was no hate or bitterness in her heart. She was perhaps too drained by the violence of the scene enacted in the tiny caravan to feel any emotion other than thankfulness that it was all over and that Rad, revealing an infinite understanding and compassion of which she would never have believed him capable, had been content just to kiss her, to draw her gently into his embrace, and quietly bid her good-night.

They travelled for the greater part of the next day, and Lynn actually enjoyed the drive, as the sun was shining, the scenery magnificent, the atmosphere between Rad and herself totally devoid of hostility. She wondered how long such a condition would last, aware that it could not possibly last long, this because she herself would never ever be happy living the life of a wandering gipsy. She wanted an aim in life, a pleasant home with a garden where she could grow flowers. In short, she wanted stability with one of her own people. Thinking of Conn she felt she had come very close to making an escape, and she had not yet given up hope. For Rad had said that they might have to return to the other tribe shortly, although he gave no explanation why this should be so.

Sitting comfortably beside him while he drove the car, Lynn saw at once that driving was by no means something in which he indulged occasionally. He was an expert, driving with such ease that it amounted almost to nonchalance. She watched his hands, those long, beautifully shaped hands so different from those one would expect of a gipsy. He turned swiftly, slanting her an interrogating glance.

'What are you thinking?' he was asking a few seconds later, having applied all his attention to a cyclist who seemed liable to swerve close to the car.

'I was thinking of your driving,' answered Lynn frankly. 'You're obviously used to handling a vehicle of some kind.'

'I've driven a fair amount,' he returned casually.

'But I seem to remember your saying that you used horses, not cars.' His tones had been bitter on that occasion, Lynn recalled. It was as though he resented the fact that other people had the means to use cars, while he had to depend on horses. She had scarcely finished speaking when Rad, turning his head swiftly, drew his brows together in a frown.

'I said what?' he demanded, his voice clearly showing signs of puzzlement.

'You said you used horses, not cars.'

She saw his frown deepen, guessed that he was trying to recollect having said this to her. Eventually he shook his head.

'You must have imagined it,' he stated emphatically. 'If I remember correctly very little was said between you and me on that occasion.' His face had hardened into austere lines, and Lynn knew instinctively that his thoughts had switched to the second meeting, and the way she had struck out at him with her riding-crop. It angered her that he should always pass off his own dastardly act and yet dwell so much on hers. Not that hers was dastardly. He deserved it ... Her reflections broke and she frowned to herself. Somehow he no longer struck her as a man who would molest a defenceless woman without provocation. No matter how she tried, she could not see Rad being quite so overtly lustful as that.

She recalled words spoken by him last evening, words that were indistinct because they were spoken to himself, but she had managed to catch what sounded like, '... the brutal part of me...' Those words now seemed vitally significant, telling her something of the character of the man who had forced her into marriage against her will. He *knew* there was a brutal part of him, and it would seem that the *other* part of him found no excuse for this brutality. His was a Jekyll-and-Hyde character, then?—a personality of conflicting traits, some good, some evil?

Lynn slanted a glance at the firm austere profile ... and something stirred within her, some emotion that had never been experienced by her before. It was half pleasant, half fearful. She recalled vividly his treatment of her last night—the savage attack on the one hand, the gentle compassion on the other. Undoubtedly he had regretted his impulsive act in chastising her so ruthlessly and had made a concerted endeavour to make amends. This morning he had picked up the dress, noticed the dirty mark made by her feet, and he had immediately gone into the kitchen, damped and soaped her face flannel, and cleaned away the mark. After that he had used a clean towel vigorously, so that the dampness would be removed before she put the dress on. Lynn had said nothing, but had returned his smile, her own a little wavering, because of this change, of her own strange emotions, of the half fearful doubt that this kindness was really taking place.

They travelled on and on, through breathtaking scenery of lush pastures, of hills clothed with trees, of mountains rising to a clear blue sky. At last Rad said they would be stopping for a snack, and this they did when, having come through Killarney, he drove along a narrow road which eventually led to a most lonely spot by the shores of a lake, which was at the foot of Purple Mountain.

'It's beautiful!' she breathed as Rad opened the door for her to alight. 'I expect you know all the lovely places on the entire island?'

'Most of them,' he smiled.

She stood looking up into his face and in her heart there was a new unfathomable sensation. The air about her seemed suddenly to be warmer than she had known it when on her own travels, the sun's rays more softly caressing, the breeze more gentle. A lightness within her gave lustre to her eyes and brought a tremulous smile quivering on her lips. Rad, staring down into her lovely face, moved his mouth as if to speak, then closed it again. But although he could control his speech he had no control over the nerve that pulsated in his throat. What had he been about to say before drawing it back? Lynn found herself sighing, and realised that she *wanted* to hear those words, that they would have been important ... both to her and to her husband.

'Come,' he said briskly at last, 'we must make haste. We've a long way to go.'

She looked up at him in perplexity and said,

'Can't you tell me where we're going, and why?'

He shook his head decisively.

'You'll know when you get there,' he said, and bent to take something from the back of the car.

'That's just it—I won't know. I'm lost already.'

'We're south of Killarney, I told you that.' He straightened up and pointed. 'That's called Purple Mountain and this is the Upper Lake. I don't know what that forest area over there is called.'

'I know all that, but I don't know *exactly* where we are.'

'Do you need to know?' he queried.

'Not really, I suppose.' Her eyes were on the basket in his hand. She had known there was something beneath the rug she always kept in the back of her car, but she had had no idea it was a most attractive picnic basket. She could not help asking where he had got it—although she would not have done so had she stopped to think.

'I stole it, of course, like everything else,' he told her satirically and she instantly coloured, her eyes flashing angrily.

'You didn't steal it!'

He lifted his straight black brows.

'That's very vehement. Is it that you don't want to think that I'm a thief?' Subtle the tone and searching the glance. Lynn averted her head and made no answer; he had correctly guessed at her thoughts. She admitted to herself that she hated the idea that her husband was a thief.

She wanted him to be an honest man ... and a good one ... But why? she asked herself, staggered by these desires. What difference would it make to her if Rad was honest or not? One day she would escape, leave him for ever, and regain her precious freedom, the value of which she had never fully appreciated until it had been taken from her by this gipsy vagabond.

CHAPTER SIX

'CAN I do anything to help?' asked Lynn as she watched her husband tinkering with a butane stove. 'Shall I take out the cutlery?' she added, eyeing the shining knives and forks which looked suspiciously like real silver. She had told Rad that he hadn't stolen the picnic basket, but now she was having to admit that he most certainly had, simply because he could not otherwise have come by such an expensive item. She supposed he must have stolen it with the intention of selling it to some fence he knew—a man who would ask no questions so long as the article was offered to him cheaply.

'Yes, if you like—and the plates too. You'll find several different kinds of sandwiches in the polythene containers.'

'Several——!' She stared blankly at him. 'Where did you get them?' she had demanded before she had time to think. His answer, spoken in a tone of sardonic amusement, was what she expected it to be.

'I stole them.'

Lynn's eyes sparkled, yet, strangely, she was not so angered this time, having owned that, if she continued to ask that type of question, she would assuredly receive the answers he had given her. But she could not allow his words to pass without some sort of return and she found herself retorting,

'Yes, I guessed that, but *where* did you steal them from?'

Rad laughed softly, half under his breath. She felt a sudden jerk of her heart, tried desperately not to notice this attractiveness which was brought about by the laugh he gave.

'I got up in the middle of the night and raided a nearby café.'

'There wasn't a café anywhere near the camp,' returned Lynn, not bothering to ask herself why she should be entering into her husband's mood like this. The atmosphere between them was amicable and she had no wish to say or do anything that would transform Rad from the rather carefree and pleasant person he now was to the fiend who, should his vicious temper be aroused, would not hesitate to reduce her to tears.

'That's what you think.' Rad stopped for a moment, watching the steam begin to rise from the spout of the kettle. 'But you don't know the district in the way I do.'

'Did you steal the stove as well?' she queried sweetly, and for the very first time she saw a twinkle of sheer amusement enter his eyes.

'Now that was far more difficult. It's heavy, as you can imagine, and as I happened to drop it on my toe, I found I couldn't run as fast as the policeman who was following me. However, although his speed was greater his stamina failed to match it and he gave up, much to my relief. I'd no wish to find myself in prison.' Stooping, he took up the kettle and made the tea. 'Did you take out the sandwiches?'

'No, but I will.' There were some of chicken and ham, some of salmon with tomato and cucumber, some more of delicious cheese. A pretty porcelain jar with a tight-fitting lid contained fresh fruit salad, and another the cream to go with it. 'It's a feast!' Lynn could not help exclaiming. 'I can't think how you managed to gather all this together—— No, don't say anything about stealing,' she said severely as he was about to interrupt. 'I've come to the conclusion that there's something very curious about you—something which, you will admit, doesn't fit in at all with your gipsy background.'

For a long moment it seemed that he would not speak, but at length his hand went automatically to the scar which was still there, on his cheek.

'But you've said I'm a gipsy vagrant, the dregs of society.' He spread his hands, opening wide his long brown fingers. 'It's all patently clear—or should be.' He paused, regarding her with an expression which held none of the fury she expected as a result of his remembering her insults. 'Why are you so interested anyway?' he wanted to know, putting the teapot down on the grass. 'After all,' he continued, straightening up, 'it *is* your affirmed intention to try to escape from me rather than to make your life with me.' Half statement but definitely a question as well, and Lynn knew a tingling of her nerves which she failed to understand. Nevertheless, there did emerge one clear and startling fact: Rad wanted her to be with him for the rest of his life!

Why she should have harboured the idea that he would tire of her she did not ask herself; it was an eventuality which she had taken for granted simply because it seemed impossible that a man of Rad's passionate nature would remain faithful to one woman. Men such as he needed change, needed the fire of youth, and this could only be obtained by leaving one woman to take on a younger one, right through their lives. He spoke again, this time to ask directly, 'Is it still your intention to make an attempt to escape?'

'Of course,' she answered without either hesitation or thought. 'What else can you expect?'

Rad's mouth seemed to move spasmodically, and he turned from her, to hide his expression, she felt sure.

'Despite the bad beginning we made,' he commented at length, 'I believe we could manage to live amicably together.' He paused, and Lynn with a back-switch of memory recalled his saying something of the sort on a previous occasion. 'After all,' he went on, spreading the rug which he had already brought from the car, 'we've been tolerably compatible today.'

'One day? That isn't much to go on.'

'It's a start; it's also an example of how we could get along.' There was no arrogance in his voice such as Lynn had heard on so many occasions. And if she did not know her husband so well she would have believed that he was actually pleading with her. Pleading...! Absurd, impossible idea! Rad would command, order, never ask even, much less plead!

'I have no intention of living the roving existence which would be my lot if I stayed with you. Besides, I'm not in love with you, so the question of my staying can't possibly arise.'

No comment from her husband; it would seem that the subject was closed, since he spoke of something else, this after inviting her to sit down and handing her a plate.

After pouring the tea Rad sat down beside Lynn on the rug. He had given no explanation for the delicious food and Lynn knew he would not do so. So she made no further reference to it until Rad portioned out the fruit and cream, and even then she merely remarked that it was good. He nodded absently, his eyes focused on the still, cool waters of the lake. It was a lonely spot, thought Lynn, here among the lakes and mountains. The sun was hot on her face and body, the hum of insects most pleasing to her ears.

She was amazed to discover that she was tolerably content, that peace enveloped her, that her husband's presence was not abhorrent to her. She glanced at his profile and despite herself she caught her breath. He was undeniably handsome, with noble features which she felt she would never reconcile to those of a gipsy. Yet there was the swarthy skin, the wild look which his curly hair gave him. And there was the unbridled passion of his emotions—temper for one thing and his physical demands for another. He turned, as if aware of her eyes upon him, and she found it difficult to remove her gaze from those fine, compelling eyes with their long black lashes.

After a while she broached the subject of their journey, asking how far they still had to go.

'A good many miles,' was his non-committal reply, and Lynn frowned as she retorted,

'That's no answer. Surely you can be a little more explicit than that?'

'About fifty miles, I should say.' Rad picked up the container from which he had taken the fruit. 'There's a little left if you would like it?'

'Thank you.'

'More tea?' he asked after she had finished the fruit.

Lynn shook her head, wondering why she should be embarrassed by her husband's meticulous attention to her needs.

'No, thank you.'

'Then we'll clear all this up and be on our way.'

She gave an audible sigh.

'I wish I knew why you had to move around like this?' she murmured in a complaining tone.

'I have a most excellent reason, I assure you.' Rad stood, obviously waiting for her to let him have the rug. She rose, at the same time picking up the teapot.

She walked to the edge of the lake and threw the rest of the tea into it, glancing around at the wild loneliness of the situation. No chance of attempting an escape here ... but she did wonder that the idea of escape had not once occurred to her since coming here, to this isolated place which her husband obviously knew so well.

Rad, too, must have thought it strange that she had not tried to make a run for it because, once in the car and on their way, he commented on it.

She thought for a space and then replied quite frankly,

'It was no use; you would obviously have run faster that I would.'

He seemed faintly amused.

'That's so,' he agreed, coming from the quiet side road on to another, wider road, but one which was certainly not a trunk road. 'However, there were several occasions when you might have had a try—when I was moving back and forwards to the car, for instance.'

'You'd have caught me,' she said resignedly. And then she added, just as if she had to, 'And I expect you'd have made me suffer.' She happened to be watching his profile, so she noticed him flinch at her words. But he said nothing and for a long while no word was spoken between them. It was when, on a narrow lane along which Rad had turned the car, a gipsy encampment came into view that Lynn spoke, asking if this was their destination.

'No,' Rad said with a slight shake of his head. 'However, I might as well have a few words with my friends.' The car slid to a standstill close by the nearest caravan. 'Stay inside,' he ordered quietly. 'I shan't be many minutes.'

Alert now to the possibility of escape, Lynn just

nodded meekly and leant back in her seat, watching Rad as he got out of the car. Several dark-skinned men came towards him, having come from their caravans, and soon there seemed to be a serious conversation going on. Lynn, feeling for the handle of the door, flicked it as quietly as she could, holding her breath in case Rad should look her way. She noticed that the men were in turn sending curious glances towards the car and the more she considered the possibility of escape the less optimistic she became. It was no use, she decided at last, for it was plain that she would be chased not only by her husband but by these others as well. What Rad had told them she could not guess, but she was certain that they were all loyal to him and would see that the woman did not escape him. After managing to flick the door to again without attracting attention, she then wound down the window. They were speaking in Romany! Lynn actually ground her teeth in frustration. If only she could hear what was going on she felt sure it would be of some value to her.

And then another figure appeared, that of a much older man, and to her surprise he spoke in English, saying, before even glancing at the car,

'He's not been here, Radulf. Give up, boy, and let him go his own way. I've advised you so many times——' His words were cut by something which Rad said. The old man glanced towards the car and from then on he spoke in the language used by the others.

Rad returned quite soon. Lynn, scanning his face as he got into the car, noted the taut mouth and jaw, the air of determination about him.

He merely glanced at her as he took the wheel, but before pressing the starter he realised he would soon be needing petrol. The car had been full at the start of the journey, and it was plain that Rad had taken it out last evening and got it filled up—and at the same time procured the picnic basket and its contents. He got out of the car after beckoning to one of the gipsy men.

'Take the car and fill it up,' he said, at the same time holding open the door for Lynn to get out. For her it was another hope dashed, since it had occurred to her that an opportunity of escape might come when Rad needed to draw into a garage and fill up the tank. He was now holding her hand, an unnecessary precaution since she had no intention of making a run for it which could only end in failure.

'You appear to have plenty of money,' she remarked, seeing him take a note from his wallet to pay for the petrol.

'Stolen,' returned Rad briefly, and this time there was no humour in his voice. He was too preoccupied by something told to him by the gipsy men. That he was searching for someone was now perfectly plain; the old man's words, coupled with what Olave had said, combined to give Lynn more than she needed as regards clues. But this new knowledge did nothing to clear up the mystery which she knew surrounded her husband. On the contrary, it merely posed another question: who was Rad looking for? Lynn could have gone on and asked *why* her husband was looking for this man, and from there asked what he intended to do when he had found him—if ever he did find him, that was. Olave had stated that he was elusive, and this was evident; what was also evident was that Rad was not the person to give up easily. It wouldn't have surprised his wife to learn that he was willing to cover the length and breadth of the island in his search. What added enormously to the mystery was the fact that he appeared to have money and to spare for his scouring of the countryside.

If he *were* intending to scour the countryside, then surely there would come, at one time or another, the opportunity for Lynn to effect an escape.

At last the camp was reached, but by this time dusk was falling and already a drift of stars penetrated through the branches of the trees. The camp was situated in the most beautiful setting of mountains and lakes, of woods and undulating hills clothed with lovely trees such as Japanese larches, sitka spruce and contorta pines.

As before, gipsy men, women and children came out of their caravans, murmuring in their own language. Rad, speaking in Romany, soon had them all exclaiming excitedly and looking at Lynn as she was led—with her husband's grip firm on her arm—to one of the caravans. It was impossible to tell whether or not Rad had been expected, but there was no doubt about his welcome, or that he was comfortably at home among the people of this tribe just as he had been by those of the one they had left.

'How long shall we be staying here?' Lynn spoke sharply as Rad closed the door on the people outside. 'I feel like some freak on exhibition at a fair!'

He frowned but showed no anger.

'You'll not always be a nine-days' wonder. They'll all become used to you in time.'

'Weren't they surprised that you're married?'

Faintly he smiled.

'Not only surprised, my dear, but amazed.'

'You've been regarded as a confirmed bachelor, I suppose!'

'That's right,' he returned mildly, 'I have.'

'It's a great pity you didn't stay that way!' She was filled with self-pity again, the pleasant day she had spent being over and done with—no more than a memory. Here, she would return to her role of prisoner, confined to this caravan which, she had to admit, was far superior to the other, being of the modern type. Nevertheless, she *was* a prisoner, and the prospect erased all the pleasure of today and brought back the misery and hopelessness she had known since that never-to-be-forgotten day when she had met up with this dark unfathomable man whose wife she was destined to become.

'What's the matter with you?' snapped Rad. 'I've never met anyone with a more unpredictable temper than yours!'

Her blue eyes opened very wide.

'What about yours?' she demanded. 'It's as vicious as that of a wild animal!'

'I said—unpredictable,' he corrected shortly, then glanced around. 'This isn't too bad. There's a wardrobe, I see. I'll fetch your suitcases from the boot of the car.' He himself had acquired a case from somewhere and he carried this in as well. Lynn watched fascinated as he brought out two immaculate shirts and a white sweater. He had underwear, pyjamas, towels and everything else one needed when travelling around the country. Sensing her deep interest, Rad looked up from his unpacking, a hint of sardonic amusement curving his lips.

'Yes, Lynn, I was exceedingly busy last night while you were asleep in bed. I stole all this from——'

'You can cut out the explanations!' flashed Lynn, totally uncaring if his anger should be aroused. 'I'm not in the least interested in how you came by these clothes—or by anything else for that matter!' She wheeled away and stood staring out of the window to the mountains, their ragged peaks softened by the rose and silver of a summer twilight. So peaceful, over there, away from the rest of the world. Tears gathered in Lynn's eyes, but it was anger that tore at her nerve-ends, anger and frustration at her utter helplessness.

'Lynn,' said Rad in a very soft voice, 'I do advise you not to rile me. It's entirely for your own good, I assure you.'

'You're threatening me again?' Lynn swung around to face him, her fists clenched at her sides. 'Go on, then! Do to me what you did last night! It's only what's to be expected from a—from a—heathen!'

Rad, who had been about to put his shirts in a drawer, straightened up, dark fury burning in his eyes. 'Must you taunt me? Must you tempt me to use violence upon you?' He took a step towards her and gripped her by the shoulders. 'Insults—all the time! When will you learn to curb your tongue?' He shook her, as if unable to control the impulse. But although rage consumed him he did seem to draw back from too primitive and unbridled an attack. Nevertheless, Lynn nursed her shoulders when presently he released her, wondering just how many more bruises he would inflict on her before she managed to get out of his clutches. 'You'd better unpack your clothes,' he said, his voice having become quietly controlled. 'We're likely to be here for some days.'

'Some days? And after that?'

'I don't know,' he sighed, 'I really don't know.'

What a change! From the violent uncivilised gipsy he was now a quiet gentleman, sounding tired and dispirited.

Lynn said, framing her words carefully,

'Are you looking for someone in particular?'

He glanced swiftly at her. Obviously he was not aware that she had overheard the old man. And of course he had no idea that she had overheard Olave talking to him on that first night.

'What makes you ask a thing like that?' he demanded.

'Well——' Lynn spread her hands, 'it's the only explanation I can find for all this running about.'

'I see...' Rad put his shirts away, then his underwear. 'I shall be going out in about an hour,' he said. 'There'll be no opportunity for you to run off; I shall have someone watching this caravan all the time.' He spoke casually, as if his subject were no more interesting or important than the weather.

'How long will you be away?' she asked shrilly. Again anger tore at her nerves. 'I shall stand at the window and scream! I can't bear it—*can't*, I tell you!'

'Don't be melodramatic,' he said impatiently. 'I don't expect to be away too long.'

'I'll—I'll smash all the windows,' she threatened. 'In fact, as I feel now I could smash everything I see!'

Her husband gave a deep sigh. She saw that he was fully aware that he had a problem, and she thought that if she could wear him down sufficiently he would be glad to let her go. Obviously he was troubled because he could not find this man he was seeking, and Lynn decided to play on *his* nerves, systematically plucking at them at every opportunity. She would pay for it, but somehow that seemed not to matter any more. Better to suffer a few bruises and escape than to endure this life indefinitely.

'I've said I shan't be long.' Rad seemed more tired than ever; she knew for sure that it had nothing to do with the long drive in the car, since he was not the kind of man to be troubled by anything like that. She guessed that he had a great deal more stamina than most men.

'Aren't you having a meal?' she asked, astounded that she should be troubled about such a thing.

He shook his head.

'Not until I come back. We'll have something together then.'

She wasn't hungry but, suddenly too spent to argue, she just sat down on the settee and waited for him to go. He appeared to be slightly hesitant. Was he worried about her? His expression certainly seemed anxious, she thought.

'Don't try anything on, Lynn,' he advised when at last he was at the door. 'You won't get away.'

'One day I will!'

'You think so?' His black eyes roved her body; she thought: he's speculating on what he'll do to me when he returns. If only I could be gone...!

'Yes, I do think so.' And she just had to add, 'And I shall carry away with me the most intolerable memories!'

She saw his mouth tighten, his hand curl tightly around the catch of the door. Why didn't he go? She was so very weary of all this backchat. Tomorrow, when she felt more fresh, she would begin her concentrated attack on his nerves.

It was almost ten o'clock when he returned. Lynn, her head buried in a cushion and her knees up under her chin, was fast asleep in one of the comfortable armchairs. Earlier, she had taken a look round the caravan, after putting away her clothes, and had been impressed by the cleanliness, the layout and the size of the van. There was a small bathroom—but of course no running water. There was a kitchen, and a separate bedroom with a dressing-table and a second wardrobe. The bedroom was small, and so, naturally, was the bed. Lynn shuddered, went to the window, and looked out. A woman was sitting on the step of her caravan. Lynn came back into the living-room and looked through another window. The same; a woman sitting in her open doorway. Obviously Rad paid them all for acting as her jailers. But where did he get the money? So many unanswerable questions. At last Lynn got into the chair, curled up, and fell asleep.

And this was how Rad found her, and as she did not wake up he stood there, looking down at her hair, flowing like a lovely veil over one sun-brown shoulder and on to the cushion. There was a brooding expression on his face and an ache in his heart. His lips moved, to form the silent words.

'A gipsy vagrant ... the dregs of society...' And he went then to the mirror, to stand examining his swarthy face, his jet black hair, unruly as ever it could be, tossed as it was by the freshening breeze coming down from the mountains. He turned slowly as his wife stirred, watched her bring her head up and open her eyes. He knew that it was a wild man she saw ... a heathen. She closed her eyes again and he saw two great tears come forth and glisten on her lashes.

'You're back at last,' she murmured, but to herself. Rad said softly, coming over to the chair,

'Is my company better than none?'

Lynn's mouth tightened. She wanted to hurt him, and so she told a lie.

'No, certainly not! The company of a person one hates could never be desirable!'

He reached for her hand and dragged her to her feet.

'God, woman, you enrage me!' His mouth claimed hers in a fierce demanding kiss. She struggled, still half asleep, and very, very tired and depressed. Her face came against the scar, which had reddened as his fury rose. Nauseated, she recoiled, and when her husband realised what had happened he took her hand and deliberately placed it on his cheek. The weal was raised and contact with it sickened her. 'I do not think,' he said in gritting tones, 'that it will be long before you receive a dose of your own medicine.'

She shivered, knowing that he would not restrict his punishment to one stroke as she had done. She thought of her resolve to play on his nerves ... and immediately gave up the idea. If her life was not going to be a prolonged hell, then she must resign herself to her husband's domination; she must not rile him, must obey his every command...

Suddenly she could see him only as she had seen him last night, tender, gentle, compassionate. If she could keep in mind that he possessed a dual personality—being a savage gipsy one moment and a gentleman the next, then life might become a little more bearable. She recalled his tiredness earlier. In fact, he appeared to be just as dispirited as she. And as she raised her head now Lynn saw again that weary look, that slight frown that seemed to tell her plainly that he needed comfort, just as she had needed it last night. To her amazement she found she wanted more than anything to give him that comfort, but knew not how to begin. Perhaps if she could have put her arms around him, as she would have done with someone she loved, then that would be all he would want—the contact of another human being who really wanted to embrace him.

He moved, and she felt his fingers tighten on her arms, drawing her into his embrace again. Resentful in spite of her desire to comfort him, she struggled automatically. The moment for them both had been lost as, inflamed by what appeared to be her loathing, Rad made her pay so dearly that she was almost swooning when after a long while he held her from him.

'I hate you,' she whispered through her sobs. 'One day I shall pay you back for all this.'

Her words had no effect on him; this was that brutal part of him of which he had spoken. With complete lack of effort he lifted her off her feet and carried her into the tiny bedroom. The door was kicked closed behind him and in the darkness Lynn, half-fainting and powerless, lay on the bed where he had put her, wishing with all her heart that she could die. He came to her, touched one breast with his lips while his hand in masterful possession curved around the other. Lynn gave a little moan of resignation as, a few moments later, her husband lay down on the bed beside her.

CHAPTER SEVEN

FROM the camp Rad and Lynn moved on to another, and another, wandering for a fortnight along the lovely country lanes, into woodland settings and through mountain passes. Lakes and rivers contributed their own particular beauty to the landscape and if it hadn't been that she was ever conscious of her loss of freedom, Lynn could have been happy touring the island with her husband. For, since that night when his brutality had come to full vigour, he had never again touched her, always sleeping on the couch and leaving her the bed. His attitude towards her was one of kindness and consideration, but inevitably there were occasions when, reminded by some slip of the tongue on his wife's part that he was a vagrant gipsy, he would subject her to a scathing counter-attack, but it was never any worse than that.

It appeared to her that he was attempting to let her see only the better side of him and in so doing crushing the side which she had feared so much. The result was that Lynn was not only losing her fear of her husband, but was actually acquiring a sort of friendly affection for him. His strength was no longer formidable, his mastery not resented so fiercely as in the beginning. She and he conversed amicably for most of the time, and although she often mentioned the possibility of her freedom, and was always given a stern rebuff—Rad telling her inexorably that a wife's place was with her husband—she never experienced that impotent frustration which had dominated her life at first.

It was as if she had become partly resigned to her

life as the wife of a wandering gipsy, but at the same time she was acutely aware of a permanent feeling of expectancy, conscious of the fact that once her husband had found what he was searching for a difference would occur in their manner of living. As things were at present they had no home of their own, not even the lowliest of caravan homes. Always they were accommodated in a spare caravan belonging to someone else, and Lynn did wonder that these caravans should stand empty, waiting, as it were, for someone to come along and occupy them. It never occurred to her that the vans might have been vacated only hours before the arrival of Rad and herself, or that, once they were on their way again, the owners would move out from their temporary lodgings and take possession once more. But this was the case, as Lynn was later to learn.

'How long are we to move around like this?' she asked him one day as they were driving back in the direction of Killarney, having visited three different camps in the beautiful Ring of Kerry, although they had stayed at only one of them. At the other two Rad had merely made some inquiries and then gone on again, searching... searching...

'Not very much longer,' Rad answered, much to Lynn's surprise. 'We shall probably be in our own home within a fortnight from now.' A most odd inflection in his voice made Lynn look curiously at him. He had turned into a quiet lane and stopped the car, saying they would have a drink. This was in a flask in the back of the car and he reached over and picked it up. As always he poured Lynn's out and gave it to her before attempting to pour his own. She took it from him, her whole mind absorbed with what he had just said. Their own home...

'We'll be settling at one particular camp?' Lynn

shook her head; it was a gesture of bewilderment, since she could not even begin to understand her own feelings. She knew quite definitely that she could never be happy living on a gipsy camp ... but she knew also that, no matter how she tried, she could never—these days—imagine life without Rad. It was so absurd for her to be possessed of this confusion of mind, as there was no doubt at all that her real home was England, which she loved, and where she had always hoped to find a small house which she could make into a home. And if she found a man she could love, then that was to be a bonus. Her thoughts had often flown to Thomas, but Rad had been right when he said that Thomas would not do for her. He was too stolid by far. In travelling like this with her husband Lynn had come quite honestly to admit that the existence she had hitherto accepted as living was in fact one continuous round of dull routine.

'We most certainly shall be settling,' her husband said, breaking into her reverie.

'I don't like the idea of living in a camp.' Lynn's voice was soft—gentle, almost—and with a hint of pleading in its depths. 'Can't we live somewhere else?'

Her husband turned to her, an odd expression on his face. She noticed the hesitancy about him which had been in evidence once before and wondered what it was he would like to convey to her.

'It would appear,' said Rad slowly, as if carefully choosing his words, 'that you are now resigned to living with me?'

Lynn averted her eyes, scarcely knowing why. Yet she supposed there was something in her expression which she wanted to conceal from him. Why, she asked herself, had not a swift denial risen to her lips? This silence savoured of acquiescence, of the total loss of any desire to resist the thraldom which would surely continue if she remained the wife of this man. Suddenly the whole dark passage of her future spread out before her and involuntarily she gave a little cry of protest.

'No!' she flashed, 'I am not resigned! I shall always try to get away from you—and I'll succeed! You can't possibly watch me all the time—for years and years and years, until we're both old!' Her voice had risen to a shrill crescendo which caused her husband to flinch as the discordant notes fell upon his ears. 'Let me go—please let me go now,' she cried, spilling her tea as the strength of her emotion took effect on her body. Rad took the cup from her shaking fingers and held it in his hand, waiting for her composure to be restored. 'Let me go. I'll not get you into trouble, believe me. I'll never say a word to anyone.'

She swallowed convulsively, trying to dislodge the lump that had settled in her throat. She was worked up almost to breaking point, her nerves rioting so that her thoughts were in total chaos. Nothing was clear in her mind and she could have screamed at the numerous disconnected visions which intruded—the vision of freedom and a return to England and her job; the vision of Rad and his domination—then his kindness and concern for her comfort. Then life without him loomed as dark and forbidding as life with him. She saw this latter as an unending trek as a member of a wanderlust tribe of gipsies, and the former as a void in which she searched in vain for happiness—— A void ... But why ...?

'Oh, God help me!' she cried aloud as the truth burst in upon these visions, dissolving them so that her whole mind became clear to absorb this one momentous fact.

'Lynn, my dear, what is it?' Rad spoke sharply, but it was with concern more than impatience. 'For heaven's sake don't work yourself up like this.' She made no answer, but merely stared at him, shattered by what she had learned about her own heart. It wasn't true, she whispered to herself. It could not possibly be true. Rad spoke again, but the words passed her by, so occupied was her mind by its own revelation. A convulsive shudder passed through her, its violence such that she actually knocked against her husband's arm and the tea now spilled over on to his knee. 'Lynn ...' His voice was soft, and deeply anxious. 'Are you ill?'

She shook her head and, emerging from her trance-like state, she wondered what he would have to say should she reveal what she herself had only just discovered. Would he receive the news gladly?—or would he gloat with triumph and say exultantly,

'So you fell in love with the vagrant gipsy, eh? Well, you'll never leave me now, wife! You can't because your love makes you my slave!'

She would never tell him! Nor did this make any difference to her determination to escape. She was not living his kind of life, her children ragged and uneducated! Love must be crushed since this was a situation where the head must rule.

Confusion flooded in again as she recalled so much about Rad which was at variance with his gipsy traits; she had already reached the conclusion that he had a dual personality, and had told herself that, could she keep this in mind, then life would become more pleasant than it had been previously. She now reflected on this past fortnight and how her husband had never once made any demands on her. He had not even kissed her ... although she had sensed on many occasions that it would have afforded him profound pleasure if he had done so. But he was curbing every instinct that might lead him to a more passionate approach. In fact, he was considering her before himself...

What kind of a man was he? Even if she could tolerate the life in general she could never be happy with a man of whose personality she knew so little.

His voice drifted into her reflections and she turned to him.

'I asked if you are ill,' he said.

'No—I'm all right now.' This was the truth; she did feel more composed despite the fact that her mind was still confused. Even now, as she looked at his profile, she noticed a distinction about him which made it seem totally impossible that he could be a gipsy. Driven suddenly to speak about the wandering they had done recently, she asked outright who he was looking for.

He gave a slight start but recovered instantly.

'I seem to remember your mentioning something of the sort before?'

'I said that it was the only explanation I could see for all this moving around.' Lynn paused a moment. 'I'll be honest,' she said with decision. 'I overheard that old man saying that *someone* hadn't been to the camp, the person referred to being a man, because the next words were, "Give up, boy, and let him go his own way." It was obvious that you were searching for some man.' She thought of mentioning Olave's words too, but decided this was not necessary.

'I see...' Rad handed her back her cup. 'You didn't mention this at the time?'

'At the time that I asked if you were searching for someone, you mean? No, I thought perhaps you'd be vexed at the idea that I'd put down the car window in order to listen.'

Rad smiled reluctantly and said, veering the subject away from that of his search and, Lynn guessed, deciding it would not be reintroduced,

'Obviously you're not as afraid of my anger now as you were then.'

'No, I'm not.'

'Tell me, Lynn, are you happier now than when——' He stopped, frowning, and she guessed that he was trying to find some delicate way of finishing the sentence. She would never know how she came to have the courage to do this for him, but she did have it, putting it into her own words as she said,

'—you were making love to me?'

If Rad was surprised he hid his feelings very well indeed.

'Yes, that is what I was going to say.' He took a long drink, dropped the dregs through the open door of the car, and wrapped his cup in a paper serviette.

'I am more content,' answered Lynn quietly. But was she? It was no use denying that, during this past fortnight, she had at times found herself looking at those long brown hands of his ... and recalling that their caress had sent a quivering ecstasy surging through her body on more than one occasion—this when he'd been in a rather gentler mood than usual. Did she desire him? If so it was by no means a strange thing, but just the result of the love she had for him. Love ... She despised herself for what she considered to be her weakness. Just because for the last couple of weeks he had been kind to her, she had fallen in love with him!

But had it really started so recently? She had admitted to his attractions almost from the first moment of seeing him.

He was speaking, a shade of bitterness in his voice.

'More content, eh? So you'd be satisfied with this kind of existence for the rest of your life?'

Frowningly she shook her head.

'Your question's irrelevant. I'm not contemplating being with you for the rest of my life.'

Instead of the anger she half expected to witness Lynn merely heard a sigh. Then, changing the subject, Rad asked if she had finished with her cup.

She handed it to him; a few minutes later the car was purring along the road again with Rad, his features a rigid mask, staring straight ahead, and Lynn sunk in thought, trying to estimate just how much this trip had cost her husband in petrol and food. The sum which eventually came to her proved beyond doubt that Rad was not short of money, but Lynn no longer wasted her time in making unprofitable guesses as to how he came to possess this money.

Rad called at another camp and then, much to her surprise, he told her that they would be staying that night at a bungalow by the sea and not, as was usual, in a caravan.

'A bungalow?' She looked at him blankly. 'Whose bungalow is it?'

'It belongs to a friend of mine,' replied her husband impassively.

'You have friends who are not gipsies, then?'

'I do.'

'This bungalow—is it empty?'

Rad nodded his head.

'It's a holiday bungalow facing the sea. I'm sure you will like it.' His finely-timbred voice was low and almost caressing with its hint of a soft Irish burr. 'It has every modern convenience in spite of being miles from anywhere.'

'It's—isolated?'

'Don't cherish any ideas of escaping me, Lynn. I shouldn't be taking you there if it wasn't isolated.'

'Do people use it for holidays—I mean, are holiday-makers content to be so far from any entertainment?'

'You've hidden your disappointment very well,' said Rad in some amusement.

She looked at him with an expression of inquiry.

'I don't know what you mean?'

'You had notions of running out on me. You thought it might be easier from a bungalow than from a gipsy camp.'

'It's impossible from a gipsy camp. As for what you have concluded—I think I know you well enough to be sure you wouldn't run any risks.' She paused in case he should have some comment to make, continuing, when he remained silent, 'I can't understand a holiday bungalow being so off the beaten track as this one appears to be.'

'It's not one that is let to the public.'

'Oh, I see. It's a private bungalow?'

'That's right. My friend built it four years ago so that he could get away from it all two or three times a year.'

'He must be rich!' exclaimed Lynn, and she was extremely puzzled now, for this was something else about her husband that increased the mystery which obviously surrounded him. 'I wish I understood,' she added on a petulant note. 'If you told me something about yourself things might be different between us ...' Her voice trailed away as she saw his expression.

'Different between us? Lynn, what are you saying?' Rad had almost stopped the car and she suspected that deep emotion held him in its grip. So changed he was ... almost humble ... 'In what way different?'

Lynn shook her head, totally bewildered by his manner.

'I can't explain,' she prevaricated, not knowing herself what she had meant. Certainly she had not meant to deceive him into thinking that she would remain with him as his wife.

He seemed to sag for a second and then, jabbing at the accelerator, he sent the car speeding along the road again, driving for what seemed an eternity before, having skirted several hills and travelled along many narrow roads, he eventually turned off on to a road which, he told her, was not even on the map. She gasped at the scene of rocky cliffs and golden sands, totally deserted except for seagulls circling around as they took advantage of the thermal currents. The narrow lane continued, becoming more difficult to negotiate since the tarmac ceased altogether in the end and only a stony track remained.

At last Rad turned the car into a long drive which continued for about half a mile, both sides of it enclosed by an ancient stone wall which made Lynn think that the bungalow must have been built on the site of an older house—most probably a tiny farm cottage. Above the wall grew trees, which met overhead. The sun was still shining and the whole aspect was one of sheer unspoiled beauty. The bungalow was white, with a wide patio embellished by wrought-iron railings and numerous ornamental pots filled with flowers—fuchsias, begonias, geraniums and many others. Bordering the extensive lawn area were many unexpected species of trees and shrubs—magnolias, camellias, nothfalgus and eucalyptus.

'It's ... heavenly ...' Lynn, having been handed out

of the car by her husband, stood looking all around before her eyes at last focused on the more natural scenery of mountains and lush green hills and, in front, the Atlantic, turquoise in the distance, blue where it carelessly scattered white blossoms of foam on to a beach of gold. 'I just can't believe it!' Again she swivelled around. 'Not anything else in sight! How did your friend find a place like this?'

There was a momentary hesitation before her husband answered her.

'The land's been in his family for generations. Once there was a farm——' Rad broke off to point towards some green undulating land spreading back from the sea. 'This was two small cottages where the farm hands lived. My friend decided that this was the place to come when he wanted to get away from the cares of his work.'

Lynn said,

'What kind of work does your friend do?'

'He owns an estate,' answered Rad, and this time he spoke abruptly, as if warning his wife that quite enough questions had been asked and he was not intending to answer any more—not about his friend, that was.

They entered through the front door, Rad's having brought a key from his pocket. Lynn was soon gasping again, this time at the sheer luxury of the furnishings, the carpets and the curtains. The ornaments, too, were expensive, being of silver in the case of candlesticks and fruit bowls, and of antique porcelain in the case of vases, groups or single figures. She stood in the centre of the living room and surveyed it for a long while, some strange prickling of her senses telling her that no gipsy belonged here. And even though she tried to thrust away the suspicion, she could not help but conclude that Rad, aware that this place stood empty for most of the year, knew he could take it over for a night without any risk of being caught. But how had he come by the key? Well, that could have been easy, she thought, remembering how the key of her flat fitted her friend's front door, and *vice versa.*

Glancing at the key which Rad was idly tapping on the palm of his hand as he watched her, she saw that it was just an ordinary type of key ... and probably was not made for this particular lock at all. Gipsies, she surmised, would not be without various kinds of keys. This lonely house was just the place for anyone to squat——

'What are you thinking about, Lynn?' Rad's voice brought her from her musings and she forced a smile to her lips.

'I was thinking that it's been rigged up at very great expense,' she lied, but saw at once that her husband was not deceived.

'You were thinking that a gipsy vagrant like me couldn't possibly have a friend who owned a house like this.' His voice was edged with bitterness, but Lynn could not possibly miss the low-toned note of fury which was there as well. It was something she had not heard for some time and, strangely, it hurt her to hear it now.

'Is there a bath?' she asked, changing the subject. It would be a wonderful luxury to lie in a bath of warm water.

'Of course there's a bath.' He led the way and after showing it to her he continued around all the rooms.

'Someone must come in here to keep this place clean,' she said, glancing questioningly at him. Rad nodded and pointed towards some vague spot over a ridge of tree-covered land.

'There are two cottages behind there; one's owned by a widow who comes in each day to see if everything's all right.'

'Each day?' she repeated.

'That's right—and as she comes early in the morning you'll see that I couldn't possibly be trespassing.'

Lynn coloured at this keen perception.

'She'll be here early in the morning?' she said, seizing on this.

'She'll not be helping you to escape,' Rad assured her coolly. 'Mrs White happens to be rather fond of me.'

'You appear to have numerous confederates,' she returned tartly.

'If you want to have a bath now the water should be hot,' said Rad, changing the subject. 'I told Mrs White that I'd be coming, and requested that she have the water hot.'

'You told . . .?' Lynn stared at him in blank bewilderment. 'When did you tell her—and how?'

Rad actually laughed at her expression.

'I left a message at the camp we called at and asked that it be conveyed to Mrs White by telephone.'

'I see . . .' There was so much that she did *not* see that Lynn gave up altogether. This treat was far too tempting for her not to make the most of it.

She would have got undressed in the bathroom, but Rad smilingly told her to undress in the bedroom.

'But why?' she wanted to know.

'Because then, my dear, I can remove your clothes.'

'Oh . . .!' Her fists clenched at her sides. 'You think of everything, don't you?'

'I have to,' he rejoined smoothly. 'Would you like me to run the bath for you?'

She glared at him and made no answer. A moment

later she heard the water running into the bath.

She took longer than she intended and by the time she came into the bedroom again her temper was restored. Rad was sitting on the bed and for one fleeting second his appreciative eyes roved her lovely figure, clad only in the diaphanous negligé, which was the only garment her husband had allowed her to take into the bathroom.

'You obviously enjoyed that,' he commented, glancing significantly at the clock on the dressing-table. 'You've been in there for almost half an hour.'

'Oh ... I'm sorry.' She looked a shade distressed, but Rad reassured her at once.

'Don't worry about it, my child. I've been busy making a few telephone calls.'

Telephone calls ... So there was a telephone in the house.

She hoped she appeared casual as she asked,

'Doesn't your friend mind your using his phone?'

'Not in the least,' he replied casually.

Lynn watched him go from the bedroom, wondering who he could be calling on the telephone. Not a gipsy encampment, that was for sure!

After waiting to hear the water turned on Lynn crept out of the bedroom and entered the hall where, she supposed, the telephone would be. It was not there, so she made for the living-room.

'So...' Lynn's mouth compressed as her anger rose. The connection was there, but the telephone was missing. It was one of those telephones which could be unplugged and carried about, from one room to another. Rad had hidden it, which was only to be expected, thought Lynn, since he would know full well that his wife would not be so lax as to miss an opportunity like that, should it present itself.

She thrust away her fury and dwelt on the casual manner in which he had mentioned his telephone calls. It struck her that he was not troubling to avoid creating situations which must inevitably set her mind seething with questions about him. A great sigh of frustration escaped her; she did wish she could find some way of making him answer some of the questions that were running around in her head, causing her such intense puzzlement and doubt.

Doubt ... Of what? Lynn sat down on the bed and tried to reason out what could be the explanation of all that was so conflicting in her husband. That he was a gipsy was absolutely certain, and yet it was an undeniable fact that he had much about him that gave the impression of a gentleman through and through—and in fact Lynn had often likened him to a nobleman, so distinguished would he become both in bearing and in speech. During the latter period when they had been travelling around all the time, he had dropped completely any sign of the swaggering gipsy and even his appearance was different, helped as it was by the attractive shirts he wore and the well-cut slacks. To Lynn it was plain that, in the beginning, he had deliberately assumed a manner which would turn her against him ... but why?

Why ... *why*...! So many questions! This bungalow presented another alien piece of the jigsaw, since it was inconceivable that a gipsy would have a friend who could afford such a luxuriously-appointed house. And it was obvious that Rad had been here before, as he was perfectly at home, knowing where everything was. In addition, he had obviously had the authority to be able to send word to the woman who looked after the place and tell her that he would be arriving.

Lynn glanced up, to see her husband come in. To her surprise he wore a most expensive dressing-gown which she had never seen before. He had washed his hair but not yet combed it, and she frowned a little and saw him only as a wild gipsy totally out of his element in this refinement.

'Sorry about my appearance,' he said smoothly, and it was plain that he had caught on to her thoughts. 'I shall improve with a little attention to detail.'

'There's no need for such sarcasm,' she almost snapped. 'Do you mind if I have my clothes now? It isn't too warm in here.'

'You're cold?' Without hesitation he snapped a switch and an electric fire began to send forth its heat. 'I'll turn on the central heating in a few moments, when I'm dressed.' Moving to a locked wardrobe, he produced a key, unlocked the door and threw it open. 'You'll find your clothes in there, also your suitcases.' He paused a moment. 'I believe I saw a long dress in one of your cases?'

'What about it?' Lynn's eyes were on the dressing-gown. If it belonged to the owner of the house then he must be the same size as Rad. Even the sleeves were right—and Rad had particularly long arms.

'I'd like you to put it on,' answered her husband quietly. His black eyes were on her, taking in the beauty which was so seductively portrayed through the delicate material of which her negligé was made. We shall eat in style this evening.'

About to protest, Lynn changed her mind. Firstly, she was most curious to learn just what he meant by 'in style', and secondly, she thought it would be a most wonderful treat to dress up and sit at a proper table, using cutlery that had not been provided by gipsies who cared neither for cleanliness nor for the fact that most of their utensils were fit only for throwing out. She even found herself smiling at the idea of a table-cloth, and perhaps flowers. There were plenty in the garden.

'You appear to be happy at my suggestion.' Rad gave her one of his rare smiles and, moving away from the wardrobe, took up a hairbrush from the dressing-table. 'Bring out your dress and let me see it.'

She did as she was told, amazed at her lack of embarrassment in walking about in this attire.

'I have another,' she told him after producing an evening gown of lime-green chiffon.

'Bring that out as well.' Rad took the dress and held it against her. She was acutely aware of his nearness, of his superb physique, of his magnetism; a flush rose to her cheeks and her lovely mouth parted in an unconscious invitation to be kissed. Rad's eyes flickered with an odd expression and the arrogance that was an innate part of him seemed all at once to add to his attractiveness. Quivering, and with her heart beating much too fast, Lynn had no thought in her mind except that she loved him. Nothing else seemed to matter in this profound moment of expectancy and desire. She knew that if Rad decided to take her she would not only come to him willingly but she would without stint give him of her all.

But he merely smiled, placed a light kiss on her lips and repeated his order that she should bring out the other dress.

CHAPTER EIGHT

THEY sat opposite to one another at a table lit by candles set in silver candelabra. A silver bowl, filled with roses and carnations, stood at one end and a similar bowl, piled high with fresh fruit, stood at the other. The cloth was snowy-white, the cutlery gleaming and expensive. Lynn, clad in a pretty evening dress of ivory organza, was happier than at any time since that fatal day when she and Rad had met. She knew her happiness would be short-lived, that this evening was no more than a bright interlude in the darkness of her life; she knew that although at this moment she was content to be with her husband, she had no intention of making her life with him.

By some obscure means he had managed to be here tonight, in this lovely modern bungalow which—she had discovered when, accompanied by Rad, she had wandered over the beautiful grounds—had a swimming-pool of heated sea-water, a tennis court and an ornamental lake. These were all at the rear of the bungalow and their view was to the green hills and the mountains beyond. The most idyllic spot she had ever known, Lynn decided and she ruthlessly thrust away the questions that troubled her, determined to savour every single minute of this treat which had so unexpectedly been given to her.

'You're quiet, my dear.' Softly her husband's voice intruded and Lynn smiled as she glanced at him. Immaculate in a dark lounge suit that fitted him to perfection, and with the gleaming white shirt contrasting most startlingly with his swarthy skin, he was neither incongruous in this setting nor unused to it.

'I'm enjoying it all,' she replied briefly.

'And wanting to ask me numerous questions,' he said amusedly. 'You are the most restrained woman I have ever come across.'

'Gipsies, then, are obviously more curious than women like me.' Lynn picked up her spoon and took up some of the tinned grapefruit which Rad had produced as a starter, having casually taken it from a cupboard stored to overflowing with provisions in tins.

Ignoring this, Rad said,

'Why don't you ask me some of these questions that are troubling you?'

'What makes you suppose I'm troubled?'

'It's written all over your face—— No, not trouble in the true sense, of course, but you're exceedingly puzzled by several things that have happened recently.'

'Not several things, but numerous things.' Lynn paused a moment, to eat her grapefruit. 'Are you telling me that you're now willing to answer my questions? You haven't been very helpful up till now.' Her eyes fell to the place where the show-white collar of his shirt met the swarthiness of his skin, and then to the jacket he wore. 'Borrowed' from the owner of the bungalow? It was a very strange coincidence that the two men were exactly the same size.

'Perhaps—up till now,' Rad was saying, 'I haven't felt the need to answer your questions.'

'Need?' Lynn's eyes flew to his. She little knew how alluringly the candlelight enhanced their colour, or that the reason why her husband suddenly—and quite unconsciously—laid down his spoon in its dish without having eaten its contents, was that his whole attention was caught by the lovely picture that was focused in his gaze. She did know that he was staring at her, and that for no reason at all there appeared into her mental vision that meeting with him when, leading his magnificent horse slowly towards her, he had seemed to be mesmerised by her. So strangely he had looked at her, without any of the transparent lust of that other encounter when he had terrified her by his obvious intention to do her a mischief. And so casually he had bidden her good morning, just as if she were someone he had met for the first time and with whom he was more than anxious to become friendly. For a long moment Lynn dwelt on that meeting, and wondered what difference it would have made if that really had been the first time they met.

She said at last, acutely conscious of some added bewilderment of mind, 'Are you saying that there's now some need for me to know more about you?' To her amazement she found her heart beating far too quickly, as if she were on the fringe of making a discovery that would bring her supreme happiness. It was as if an inner excitement had begun to sway her emotions and she had the firm conviction that if she could handle this new situation with a fair amount of skill, then her marriage to Rad would not be the tragedy which it at first had appeared when, brought by her kidnapper from that caravan, she had been forced into a union which might or might not be legal.

'I am certainly of the opinion that it would profit us both if I enlightened you on various matters which, quite naturally, have been most baffling to you.' The black eyes smiled faintly, but in their depths a sadness was evident, and Lynn, aware of a sudden catch at her heart, wanted desperately to say something that would effectively erase that sadness. 'However,' added Rad as a qualification to his words, 'I am not *fully confident* that it will profit us for me to answer your questions. If

I were, my Lynn, then I should do so at this very moment.'

He shook his head, and a frown came unexpectedly to his brow. Lynn had the strong suspicion that the doubt he was now experiencing had only just come to him. His next words amplified the suspicion as, softly and slowly, he said, 'I could be wrong, my dear, but during these past weeks while we've been travelling about together, I've had a feeling that there's been a change in your attitude towards me—but I'm not sure——' Again he shook his head. 'No, I'm not sure, and in consequence I dare not...' His voice faded and he picked up his spoon again.

Lynn, affected emotionally to depths she had never before experienced, glanced away, confusion mingling with a certain dejection that had come to her as a result of her husband's final words. He was not sure ... and therefore he dared not be frank about things which, obviously, he would like to tell her about himself. She felt that the opportunity had been lost, that she and Rad were not destined to make their lives together ... Together? Lynn frowned inwardly, conscious of a sort of desperation born of the desire to make a firm decision as to whether or not she really wanted to continue living with her husband. Again she saw the future as a void—should she live through it on her own, without her husband, yet on the other hand she knew without any doubt at all that she could not possibly follow the life of a wandering gipsy. She murmured at last, looking almost pleadingly at him,

'I wish you would tell me these things. I am your wife,' she added, 'and in consequence it's natural that I should want to know something about you.'

He nodded understandingly, but made no attempt to satisfy her request.

'Let's concentrate on enjoying our meal,' he said. 'It's the first one we've had together in pleasant surroundings.' His smile appeared and he was most attractive in his wife's eyes, yet she caught her lip between her teeth, disappointment flooding over her. Rad's dismissal of the subject had hurt her, and she was admitting that the pain he could now inflict upon her was far more profound than that of the past, simply because of the love that had come to her despite all the initial revulsion he had aroused within her. 'Eat your grapefruit,' he said. 'The rest of the dinner will be spoiling.'

She obeyed, then sat there while he took away the cut-glass dishes. Earlier, after she had arranged the flowers and Rad had found some candles and lighted them, she and he had made the meal together, working side by side in the large and airy modern kitchen with its electric cooker and a fridge from which Rad had taken two pieces of steak.

'I left the message that Mrs White should get them in,' Rad had explained when Lynn had asked how they came to be there. Had they been in the deep-freeze then it would have been understandable, but no meat would keep for long in the ordinary fridge.

'You appear to have thought of everything,' Lynn had said.

'I tried to. You see, my dear, I knew we would both be ready to enjoy this complete break from living on the various camps as we have been doing.'

'You—really like living on the camps, though?'

'It's a life one becomes used to. There's a freedom which is very attractive——'

'But what about the boredom?' she broke in. 'A life of idleness would drive me to distraction.'

'Gipsies are not necessarily always idle. They do

make things to sell, and they go about telling fortunes.'

'The men ... What exactly do they do—apart from sharpening knives, that is?'

He had frowned at this and made no answer, deliberately changing the subject and asking her if she had put salt in the vegetables. She sighed resignedly and carried on with what she had been doing, while Rad cooked the steaks under the grill. He had also made the side salads, with lettuce and tomatoes taken from the fridge. Lynn busied herself with a fresh fruit salad which they were to have for a dessert. Rad had actually produced some wine, his expression one of unconcealed amusement as he watched Lynn and waited for her to phrase the question which never came. She knew what his answer would have been had she inquired as to how he had come by the bottle of wine.

'I've stolen it—from the man who so kindly let me have this bungalow.'

She looked up as he returned to the dining-room, carrying a tray on which was the meat and vegetables.

'Don't get any wrong ideas,' he told her in a bantering tone as he waited on her, helping her to the steak and the vegetables. 'I shan't always wait upon you like this.'

Yet he was thoroughly enjoying himself, seeming almost like a boy as he later asked, several times, if everything was to her liking.

'It's lovely, thank you.' There was a wistfulness about Lynn which to her husband was most appealing. He smiled into her eyes, spoke gently to her, told her to drink her wine so that he could pour her some more. It was heady, but she allowed him to refill her glass, entering into a mood of sheer pleasure and expectancy and at the same time thrusting from her any thoughts which were alien to the magic of the occasion.

Much later, after they had left the dinner table and had drunk their coffee in the sitting-room, Rad suggested they go outside for a stroll.

'It will do us both good after being cooped up in the car for so long,' he added with a smile.

'Yes.' Lynn's own smile fluttered as she looked up into his dark face. She was shy all at once, and profoundly aware of her heightened emotions. 'It's a beautiful night.'

'There's a moon over the sea.'

'And stars ... millions of them.'

Her husband's smile deepened and she caught her breath. How handsome he was! And she realised that she was regarding him as a gentleman of quality rather than the vagabond gipsy to whom she was really married. It had been an evening of make-believe where, in her self-created realm of fantasy, she had pretended that this was the life she would lead from now on, living with a husband whom she dearly loved ... and who returned that love. Tomorrow would come the awakening, but tomorrow was a long way off.

'You'll need a coat,' Rad was saying. 'I'll get it for you.'

They wandered out into the grounds, into a world drenched in moonlight, where a gentle breeze wafted in from the sea to steal the flower perfumes and scatter them over the soft night air. Lynn, her coat draped over her shoulders, took deep breaths, her mind half dazed by the unreality of the whole magical scene, and definitely affected by the wine which her husband had given her. She knew her thoughts were hazy, but knew also that even if she had been able to think clearly she would have shirked doing so. This was heaven and she was in it, with the husband whom she had come to love and who, during this magic interlude, was acting very much as if he too were in love. Perhaps the wine was affecting him in the same way in which it was affecting her!

'Are you warm enough?' he asked after they had walked some way in silence.

'Yes, thank you.'

Another silence fell, a companionable silence which Lynn would never have believed possible between her husband and herself. It was as if they were true friends . . . and more.

'The sea looks so calm,' remarked Rad. 'One could swim in it on a night like this.'

'Do you swim, then?' she asked, and Rad said yes, he did, appearing to be surprised at her query. She wondered how he, a gipsy, had come to learn to swim, but she allowed the matter to pass, content as she was to be strolling beside her husband, unresentful of the fact that she was having to perform a little skip now and then when, obviously without intention, he would increase his pace.

'We'll go a little way into the hills,' Rad decided.

'You're used to the walks around here?' she murmured in response.

'Yes, I know them very well indeed.'

Should she begin asking questions? No, decided Lynn. This magical evening must be prolonged, with no dissension between her husband and herself. Artificial it all might be, but oh, how very pleasant!

The ground beneath their feet was soft and Lynn guessed that the turf had been maturing for many years. Above, a few light clouds had gathered, obscuring the moon's argent light so that a transitory shade was thrown across the path. Rad's hand sought hers; she felt the strength of his fingers clasping hers, the warmth which seemed to be relayed throughout her whole body. A total abandonment swept like a deluge over her and she trod on air, lifted to dazzling heights where the dream and the desire intermingled and the only goal must surely be fulfilment.

The clouds scudded on and once again the moonlight came into its own, sweeping across the hills and edging the darkly melodramatic backcloth of the mountains. The air was inexpressibly soft and fragrant, the distant cry of a night-bird music in Lynn's ears.

At last Rad said they should go back, and as she walked beside his tall impressive figure she wondered if her urgent need of him would be imparted to her husband. She felt her colour rise but knew no shame. To sleep in Rad's arms must surely be the crowning fulfilment to a night like this.

The telephone was ringing when they got back to the house and Rad with a swift apology ran ahead of her so that she was left to close the door. She stood looking around the moonlit landscape; so many hiding-places out there, among the undulating hills or in that thickly-wooded forest area. Her gaze swung round to the languid ocean, with the moonlight shimmering over it, creating a million diamonds that came floating towards the shore. There were the cliffs, with many fretted rock faces where there were bound to be caves ... Lynn listened, heard her husband on the telephone; she felt the cool breeze on her face, knew the temptation to run, for she had her coat, and her purse was in the pocket. Freedom ... Rad would never find her; the region of concealment was far too vast. Freedom ...

Rad was still speaking and it seemed he might continue to do so for some while yet. Whom could he be speaking to? she wondered. If the phone call had been for the owner of the bungalow then surely Rad would have been off the phone by now, having told the caller that the person he wanted was not at home. Lynn listened, but heard no more than an unintelligible murmuring of her husband's voice. He had made this one major slip and had not yet realised it, not become aware that Lynn had the opportunity of escape. She was unwatched for the first time since he had abducted her. Stupid to be standing here, undecided, with the wide open spaces all around her, and so many places where she could hide. Why was she undecided? Faintly she smiled, and her eyes glowed like stars. The magic was not ended, the lovely interlude still had a great deal to offer. With one last glance at the world outside Lynn quietly closed the door, and just as quietly shot the bolt.

Her husband was before her when she turned, standing in the wide doorway, the most odd expression in his eyes. Lynn stood motionless, her colour fluctuating as she realised what Rad must be thinking. It did not matter, she was telling herself a moment later. She was in that sort of mood which could only be regarded as total abandonment to whatever the night still had to offer. She stared at her husband across the space separating them, aware that neither he nor she had any desire to break the silence which stretched between them; the moment was far too profound for words. But after a while Rad did say the one word,

'So...' And he held out his hand to her, a smile of sheer contentment softening the hard lines that were so much a permanent feature of his swarthy countenance. Lynn's own lips parted in a responding smile, and her hand came timidly from her side, to stretch out, meeting his as both he and she stepped forward, towards one another. 'You could have gone,' he whispered in tones of disbelief. 'Out there ... I'd never have found you.' His black eyes seemed to be almost moist with pain, and Lynn realised that, had she gone from him, it would not have been anger he would have known, but a sense of emptiness and loss...

His expression changed and it was tenderness she saw now in his eyes. Something surged within her ... love for her husband ... Yet mainly her mind was a blank, as if the heady wine had triumphed over such things as mundane thoughts and recollections, and she needed no coaxing to melt into Rad's arms, laughing softly with him when, with a flourish of masterful triumph, he swung her off her feet and carried her into the bedroom.

'My Lynn,' he breathed as, setting her down on her feet, he took her unresistingly into his arms and looked deeply into her eyes. 'Is it the wine, I wonder...?' He spoke to himself, doubt in his voice. 'But no matter; the night has been magic, so we shall let the magic stay with us——' He broke off, frowning darkly as the telephone rang. Lynn, happy in the circle of his arm, looked up into a face clouded with indecision. It seemed impossible that the telephone call could be of importance to him, but Lynn knew instinctively that it was. The ringing continued, while Rad and Lynn listened. She suddenly hated the sound, hated more the person who was on the other end of the line. And then, just as she had resigned herself to Rad's leaving her, she heard his softly-spoken words, as he repeated what he had just said, 'Yes, we shall let the magic stay with us.'

Lynn gave a sigh of relief, and lifted her lips as if in

an offering for his decision. He said softly, after he had kissed her,

'You haven't ever used my name, Lynn. I'd like to hear it now.' A command despite the softness of his tone, but Lynn was so shy by now that she found it impossible to obey him. Did he understand? she wondered, because instead of pressing the matter he bent again and took her lips in a long and tender kiss. What power he had over her emotions! Desire was already strong within her, drawing her to him with a magnetic force so that she had no will to resist when, unzipping her dress, he let it fall to the floor and took one firm breast in his hand. His soft laugh would at one time have infuriated her, but now it merely brought a tender hint of colour to her face. He tilted her head with a finger under her chin, claiming her eager lips and tightening his hold until his arms seemed like steel hawsers about her slender body. He lifted her again, and laid her on the bed. No words were spoken, but mastery and surrender created the sweet poetry of love and Lynn, carried to a realm of ecstasy such as she had never dreamed could exist, gave of her all to the man whose dominance reduced her to the level of a willing slave. And when at last the slow descent from the zenith of bliss brought them back to earth, she needed no prompting from her husband for her to say his name.

'Rad ...' She turned in the circle of his arm and laid her cheek against the thick black hair that covered his chest. 'Rad ... it's an unusual name, but I like it.'

'It's very rare, and comes from the Anglo-Norman settlers in Ireland.'

'It isn't a gipsy name, then?'

Rad became strangely silent before answering her question.

'No, it isn't especially a gipsy name, if that's what you mean.'

'If it came from the Anglo-Norman settlers then it must originally have been a name adopted by the nobility of that period?'

'I expect you're right,' he agreed.

'The gipsies use it, though?'

'Obviously, since it was given to me.'

'Do you know of any other gipsies who have the same name?'

'No, as a matter of fact, I don't.'

Lynn said, after a moment of thought,

'You haven't ever mentioned your parents, Rad. Are they not still alive?'

'No, they're both dead.' No expression now in his voice—except a hint of regret, she decided.

'Tell me about your mother, please.' Lynn snuggled closer, and put her hand on her husband's cheek.

'My mother died when I was born.'

'Oh...! I'm sorry...'

'It's nothing to be sorry about. I naturally felt no loss.' Again Lynn noted regret, in spite of the way he had passed off the matter so lightly.

'So you're alone in the world?' she said. 'You didn't have any brothers or sisters?'

Again there was a silence before Rad said,

'You've obviously taken that for granted.'

A little startled, Lynn asked if he did have any brothers or sisters.

'I did take it for granted,' she added. 'I suppose it was because you strike me as a—well, as a loner.'

The ghost of a smile caused his cheek to move under her hand.

'I was a loner, I suppose—until my marriage.'

He hadn't answered her question and she asked it

again. Rad replied this time, telling her he had a brother.

'Oh, that ought to be nice for you. Where is he?'

'With another gipsy band.'

'Don't you ever see him?'

'I haven't seen him for some time,' replied Rad, and then, so abruptly that the change in his voice came as a shock to Lynn, 'It's time we were asleep. Good night—and pleasant dreams.'

Lynn said, almost fractiously.

'I don't want to go to sleep yet awhile.'

'Why not?'

She hesitated, scarcely able to tell him that the whole evening and the night had been so magical to her that she could have prolonged the interlude for ever, were that possible.

'I'm not tired,' she said, and then, before he had time to comment on this, she reintroduced the subject of his name, asking if it had any particular meaning. 'Many of the ancient names do have a meaning,' she went on, 'and they can be quite fascinating.'

'I fear you'll not be fascinated by the meaning which attaches to the name of Radulf,' he returned with a hint of amusement to his voice. 'It means "swift-wolf".'

'Swift-wolf...' Lynn recalled that swift careering through the forest on that fateful day when she had struck Rad with her crop. The scar was still very plain and she did wonder if he was marked for life. 'It's a rather frightening name,' she said at last, aware that Rad was waiting for her response to the information he had given her.

'It's all very nonsensical,' he told her. 'And so, my Lynn, we won't talk about it any more.' He kissed her on the lips, lifted a hand to switch off the muted, rose-coloured bedside light, and then, in the darkness, he bade her another tender good night and within what seemed no more than half a minute, he was sleeping peacefully, his arm still enfolding his wife.

The following morning they were up early, and having breakfast on the verandah when the telephone rang.

'The call I should have taken last night,' said Rad, rising at once. 'I shan't be many minutes, but do have yours,' he added with a glance at her plate. 'There's no sense in letting your food get cold.' He left her, to return in less than three minutes, his face a study of concern.

'What is it?' asked Lynn breathlessly, conscious that her nerves were tensed, as if Rad had conveyed his anxiety to her. 'You look so troubled.'

'It's nothing you would understand,' he began when she interrupted him, asking how the phone call came to be for him and not for the owner of the property.

'Did someone know that you'd be here?' she added.

'Of course,' impatiently. 'I had a call last evening.'

'From whom?' she asked tautly. And, when he did not give her an immediate answer, 'You're always so mysterious, Rad. Anyone would think I was a stranger instead of your wife.'

His black eyes should have warned her, by their change of expression, that he was in no mood for answering her questions. But Lynn was troubled for him and in consequence she spoke sharply, again asking him who had telephoned him last evening.

'You wouldn't be any the wiser were I to tell you.'

She looked at him, biting her lip. An idea had come to her and she tried to shake it off. Could Rad be engaged in some shady dealings? So much would be explained ... The money he always had, the clothes.

There was that magnificent horse he had been riding, there was his access to this luxurious house ... Could it be his own property? Surely not, since there was no doubt at all that he was a gipsy. Could he be leading a double life? That would be too melodramatic and she instantly dismissed it as impossible.

'I have to go out, Lynn,' Rad said, breaking into her thoughts. 'You'll not leave me? Promise?'

'I want to come with you!' Unconsciously she stamped her foot, determined to go with him, if only to try to discover something about him. He was shaking his head and she accepted that he had no intention of allowing her to accompany him. And, quite suddenly, she was calm, her whole mind on one thing—escape. She could never settle down with him for life, so what good would her love do her? The existence he followed was not for her. Much as she cared she had to leave him, to go her own way ... to seek a divorce and make a complete break. Tears pressed for release, but she valiantly kept them locked behind her eyes. He spoke again, asking if she would promise not to try to escape. She hesitated, unable to lie spontaneously. This was her undoing; without hesitation Rad took her by the shoulders, propelled her into the house and then into the bedroom. The door was locked on her and even though she hammered on it it was to no avail.

She looked at the window. Rad had made his second mistake. But then he was greatly troubled, so it was not to be expected that he would think of everything.

After unfastening the window Lynn put on her coat. Then she threw a few things into her shoulder-bag, and made her exit from the room.

The sun was bright, the sea smooth; all seemed so tranquil, and Lynn could not help remembering every detail of the happy time she had spent only a few hours earlier. Now, everything was back to normal and she was effecting the escape which, for a short time, seemed to have lost its importance. If only Rad had been an *ordinary* man!—a working man whose aim in life was to be happily married with a home and children ... Tears came to Lynn's eyes and for one wild impulsive moment she wanted to turn back, to resign herself to being the wife of a man whose activities would always be kept a secret from her. Common sense prevailed, however, and, drying her eyes, she determinedly walked on, into the shrubbery of the garden, from where she believed she could find a way on to the road. But just as she was entering the shelter of the shrubs she heard the telephone again and on sudden impulse she turned and ran back to the house where, crouching against the wall close to the window of the sitting-room, she could hear what her husband was saying.

'... good of you, Olave and I shall pay you well, my friend. He's coming here, you say? Well, at last I shall ...' Lynn lost the rest, much to her chagrin. 'I was in despair, Olave—I was sure he would have ended up in prison. If I can only talk to him, persuade him to ...' Again the words of her husband were lost to Lynn and she ground her teeth in vexation. Would she never know what was going on? She had come so close to it, she felt sure, but it seemed that Rad either lowered his voice or he moved away from the window. However, she was soon hearing his voice again, and now she ventured a little closer to the side of the big picture window, pressing her slim body against a shrub growing up the wall. 'I've no need to go out now—yes, Colum rang me a few minutes ago, telling me that Albán was at the Erevans' camp down in the valley here, and I was going there to see if I could manage to catch him before he ran out on me again. However, if he is coming here so much the better ...' Another stop, but this time Lynn concluded that it was Olave who was speaking. If only she had been able to hear the whole conversation! When Rad spoke again his voice was indistinct and Lynn had the greatest difficulty in hearing what he was saying.

'... can only hope he doesn't realise that I myself might be here ... stayed before, with that wench of his ... yes, he must have let it out that he intends to come here, because otherwise you wouldn't have heard ... so grateful to you, Olave, for letting me know. I shall never be out of your debt—— No, don't say that! I must show gratitude!'

What did it all mean? Lynn was asking herself as she waited expectantly for her husband to speak again. One thing was sure: she had no intention of leaving, not until after this Albán had called and she had taken a look at him. Somehow, she felt that the whole aspect of her future would be changed by the coming of the man for whom her husband had been so diligently seeking.

'... yes, I would have taken your advice, Olave, and given up. I have obligations now and it isn't fair to ...' The trend became lost even yet again, but what she had already heard made Lynn's heart give a little jerk, for it did seem that in using the word 'obligations' Rad was thinking about his wife. '... as you know, defeat infuriates me and it would have been hard to abandon my search. However, if I can meet Albán here, and talk to him, then I'm optimistic enough to believe I can put everything right.'

That was all Lynn heard; she decided to return to the bedroom before her husband finished the conversation which, she suspected, was already almost at an end. But luck was not with her, for as she turned towards the rear of the bungalow she caught her foot in an exposed tree root and fell headlong on to the concrete path, involuntarily crying out as her head hit the ground. Rad was there in no time at all, lifting her up and carrying her into the house.

'Oh, my head!' She felt dazed, but even so she could not miss the expression on her husband's face. It held a mingling of fury and sadness ... a strange combination, but one which she could easily explain. She had let him down, since he had been sure, despite the fact of his locking her in the bedroom, that she would not—after last night—be bent on escape. As for the fury—well, that was even more easily explained than the sadness, and Lynn waited for the reprisal which she felt sure would come. To her surprise Rad suppressed his anger and seemed concerned only with the lump which was swiftly rising on her forehead.

'You've given yourself a nasty bump. I'll get something to put on it.' He looked at her as she lay against the cushions on the couch. 'You've a headache, obviously.'

'Yes ... Rad ...'

'Well?'

'I wasn't trying to escape. On the contrary——'

'Don't lie!' he broke in sharply. 'What about this bag?' He opened it, saw its contents and lifted his black eyes in a glance of accusation which caused Lynn to hang her head. How could she explain? After all, she had initially meant to run away, and she certainly would have done so had she not heard what Rad was saying over the telephone.

'I wish I could explain,' she murmured, wincing as a pain shot through her head. 'It's so difficult.'

'It would seem that you have no intention of ever willingly making your home with me.' Rad paused, but not long enough for Lynn to find anything to say. 'The dregs of society . . .' He spoke softly, to himself, his eyes narrowed so that their expression was lost to his wife. 'I suppose the whole thing was doomed to failure. It couldn't have been otherwise.'

'Rad . . . what is it all about?' Her voice was pleading and in her eyes a look of bewilderment which successfully hid the love and the anxiety which Rad would otherwise have seen there.

'Does it matter?' he rejoined bitterly. 'You consider me beneath you, so there's only one way in which——' He broke off, listening intently as he thought he heard a sound coming from the garden. He was soon speaking again, repeating what he had just said about her considering him to be beneath him, and Lynn stared wonderingly at him, profoundly conscious of his humility, which was so very different from that arrogant air of superiority which had characterised his attitude when first she had called him the dregs of society. His fury then had been terrible to see, so uncontrolled did it become.

And now he was actually humble . . .

Lynn, filled with a guilt which dragged at her conscience, spoke softly to him, reminding him that, on the previous evening, he had come very close to confiding in her.

'If you could tell me now——' she began, but stopped as he shook his head.

'It would do no good. But I have a plan,' he continued, 'which I hope will appeal to you. However, now is not the time for discussing it. I'll get you the tablets, and then you must go to bed.'

Frustrated and with anger rising. Lynn rose from

the couch and paced the floor, feeling she could willingly have thrown one of those beautiful ornaments at her husband, so infuriatingly secretive was he with her. Rad returned, lifting his straight black brows in a gesture of inquiry.

'Why can't you tell me what's going on!' she blazed. 'I have a right to know!'

'A right?' Rad stood still, a glass in one hand and a small bottle of tablets in the other. 'What right, may I ask?'

'I'm your wife!'

Reluctantly he smiled, but it was a smile of bitterness and this was reflected in his tone when he said,

'You've never really considered yourself as my wife, Lynn, so I'm not able to confide in you.'

'Last evening—you were going to confide then.'

'Last evening I had somehow got the wrong ideas about you,' he said. 'I felt that you'd changed your opinion of me during these past few days—while we were travelling around. I had somehow gained the impression that you didn't hate me as you had in the beginning——' Suddenly he broke off, coming towards her and handing her the glass. 'Let's not talk about it, Lynn. Take these two tablets and let me get you into bed. I ought to bathe that bruise, I think.'

'It'll be all right,' she snapped pettishly. 'And I do not feel like going to bed!'

'Nevertheless, you will oblige me by doing so,' returned her husband imperiously. 'We shall be staying here today——'

'What for?' she demanded, keeping from her voice the fact that she knew full well what they were staying for.

'That, Lynn, is my business.' So quiet, so dignified. How could he be a gipsy? And yet he was one; of that

Lynn had far more proof than was necessary.

He was watching as she took the tablets, then, placing the glass on the table after she had given it back to him, he told her to go to bed. She stood her ground, fully aware that he would coerce her into obedience and yet determined to put up some sort of resistance. She reverted to last evening, asking again why he could not now confide in her.

'Because,' he answered quietly, 'your opinion of me hasn't changed. You've proved this by your attempt, just now, to run from me. I'm not good enough to be your husband ... even though you're now able to enjoy the physical side of our marriage——'

'Enjoy!' she repeated, driven by anger to say things she did not mean. 'No such thing! What an inflated opinion you have of yourself!'

The black eyes did not blaze, as she fully expected them to. They held only contempt, and Lynn found herself once again lowering her head, ashamed of the lie she had told him.

'I repeat, Lynn, you are now able to enjoy my love-making. I give you all that you need, but only physically. Mentally and spiritually you are of the opinion that I'm not on your level.' He tilted her head as he spoke, his finger under her chin. The black eyes flickered, and he nodded his head in a slow movement that spoke volumes. 'Admit it,' he commanded, suddenly imperious and masterful. 'I shall make you, believe me—even though you are not feeling quite yourself!'

He meant it, too, and Lynn bit back the angry retort and said meekly,

'All right—if it satisfies you, then I do admit it.'

'Not a very satisfactory admission,' he commented. 'Still, there'll be other occasions when I shall find you more pliable. Meanwhile, to bed!' He paused a moment and then, 'I'm sorry to do it, Lynn, but I must fix the shutters to the window. You'll be in the dark, but that won't be such a bad thing, not with your feeling the way you do.'

'Shutters?' she repeated. 'I never noticed any shutters.'

'They are not permanent fixtures,' he told her. 'They're kept for those occasions when the gales blow in from the sea.'

'Must I have them?' To be shut in, with no light ... 'I'll promise not to escape——'

'The shutters will be put up,' he broke in, and that was the end of it as far as any argument was concerned. A quarter of an hour later Lynn was lying in bed, the only trace of light entering the room coming from a chink in the centre fastening of the shutters which her husband had fixed up from the outside of the window.

CHAPTER NINE

LYNN awoke with a start, aware that the bedroom door had opened softly, letting in the light.

'I'd no intention of going to sleep,' she murmured before Rad could speak. Had the man Albán already been and gone? she wondered, her spirits dropping at the idea. 'What time is it?'

'Lunch time—one o'clock. How are you feeling now?' He came into the room and she searched his face. No, Albán had not been, Lynn felt sure.

'Much better, but I wasn't ill—just shaken by my fall,' she said.

'Are you ready for something to eat?'

'Yes, I think so.' She sat up, her gaze meeting his, and somehow she did not mind at all when his eyes moved, to take in the lovely curves of her breasts. 'What are we having?'

'I've done some fish which I found in the deep-freeze.'

She said softly,

'I expect you make a list of what you use and then pay your friend for it all?'

Rad smiled down at her as he replied,

'No, I just steal it.'

'Why do you have to talk like that!'

'Why, for that matter, do you have to ask questions which you know will be answered in my own particular way?'

'What an enigma you are,' she complained, frowning at him. 'I've already realised that you have a dual personality.'

'You have? Tell me more of this discovery?'

'You can be kind,' she said, 'or you can be brutal.'

'Brutal...?' He lifted a finger unconsciously to touch the scar which was still so clear upon his cheek. 'You've driven me to acts which I would never have thought possible.'

Lynn coloured, acutely conscious of the fact that she always felt guilty whenever the scar was brought to her attention, either verbally or as now when her husband touched it. Yet, as always, she told herself that he had deserved it—yes, and more! He was a strange man and no mistake, for as she looked at him now, standing by the bed, tall and straight and with those harsh lines softened by his thoughts, she could not by any stretch of imagination visualise his making that attempt to inflict on her the supreme injury. But he *had* made the attempt, and he would assuredly have succeeded had it not been for his gipsy girl-friend. Where was she now? wondered Lynn. At every camp they had visited she had looked out for her, but she was not there. This was another strange circumstance connected with Rad: he seemed to have dispensed with the girl without the least degree of trouble ... and yet, at the time of the incident, it was his obedience to the girl's command that had brought about Lynn's escape.

Rad was speaking, breaking into her thoughts as he reminded her that the lunch was ready.

'If you like,' he added, 'I'll bring yours in here to you.'

Lynn shook her head at once. She was eager to get up, so as not to miss the arrival of Albán. Would Rad allow her to stay while he was speaking to this man? Lynn began to doubt it, suddenly realising that he was more likely to lock her up in the bedroom again, and leave the shutters up as they were at present. Catching her underlip between her teeth, she did wonder why this possibility had not previously occurred to her. She should have made her escape, she decided, while she had the chance.

It was while they were having lunch that she said, looking seriously at Rad across the table,

'This plan you mentioned? Are you willing to discuss it now?'

For answer he shook his head, and glanced at the clock. Lynn guessed at once that the non-arrival of Albán was troubling him, that he was now in some doubt as to whether the man would once more prove to be elusive.

'Later—when things are more—settled.' A hardness crept into his tone and although Lynn would have liked to pursue the matter she knew her husband well enough to be sure that she would be wasting her time. What did he mean by the expression 'more settled'? she wondered, and sighed in exasperation at her inability to solve even one small part of the mystery surrounding this man who, from the first, had baffled her by his twisted personality.

'We might have to stay here another night,' he was saying quietly, and yet a little impatiently as well. 'But I don't suppose you'll mind that?' he added with the ghost of a smile.

'I'd rather be here than in one of those gipsy camps, naturally.'

He nodded, and she thought he frowned to himself ... as though he hated the idea of her being in a gipsy camp!

'We shall again dine like civilised people.'

Lynn's eyes flew to his.

'You don't sound like a gipsy when you talk like that,' she said.

'Don't I?' curiously as his gaze became fixed upon

her face. 'I am a gipsy, though; make no mistake about that.'

Lynn examined his swarthy features, his curly black hair that was so often unruly, his eyes which she had learned so well to read in their varied expressions—the fury and the desire, the more heated passion when these two qualities fused to bring out the primitive traits which had characterised his lovemaking at first. She had more recently read kindness in those eyes, sadness and regret. And now they held a challenge, as though he were waiting for her to deny that he was speaking the truth when he declared he was a gipsy, for he was well aware of her bewilderment, of the hundred and one questions which even a much less intelligent person than she must inevitably have asked herself. She said, bypassing the challenge,

'Is there any particular reason why we're staying on here for another night?' She guessed, of course, that Rad meant to wait for Albán, and if the man did not put in an appearance today then Rad would stay on in the hope that he might put in an appearance tomorrow. From what she had overheard Lynn knew that the man came here occasionally 'with that wench of his', so it would appear that he too had permission to use the bungalow.

'I'm expecting a visitor,' answered Rad, amazing her by the admission.

'You are?' with feigned surprise. 'A man?'

Rad nodded and for a moment said nothing as he concentrated on his food.

'Yes, a man,' he said eventually.

'It's strange that you should be having visitors.' Lynn avoided his gaze as she bent to take up a piece of fish on her fork. She was half afraid that, should she look up, she might reveal to her husband that she knew far more than she was supposed to know.

'Many things are strange to you,' he returned matter-of-factly. 'They'll be explained later, when I put my plan to you.' To Lynn's amazement his voice seemed to falter—to quiver in fact, as though a great fear had taken possession of him ... a fear that this plan of which he spoke would not meet with her approval!

'I'm so frustrated by all this mystery!' she cried, revealing her thoughts in wrathful accents. 'I can't see why there's such need for it!'

'There wouldn't be if...' He stopped, and a hand went instinctively to his cheek. 'If you didn't regard me as the dregs of society.' Such bitterness in his voice! It had been there before, many times, but never as strong as it was now. Nor had those eyes been so broodingly sad, or that mouth so uncontrollably twisting, keeping time with the pulsation of a nerve in his throat. Emotion gripped him, violent emotion that he could not hold in check. It seemed to convey the message that his whole life was in danger, his future threatened with perpetual darkness...

Lynn, herself gripped by tension, managed to keep her voice reasonably casual as she said, her love for him rising above all else,

'Has it never occurred to you that I might have changed my ideas about that? I said it when under great stress, if you remember?' She knew she was pale, knew she was fighting for something ... but what? 'People say things they afterwards regret—just as they do things they afterwards regret.' She was referring to his own unbridled passions on that night when, goaded by fury, he had resorted to physical violence. She had no doubt at all that he regretted his action, and that it would be a long time before he could forget it. He was staring at her across the table, a question in his eyes. 'To a great extent,' Lynn went on, 'I've revised my opinion of you. Oh, I know you have this dual personality, that you possess that brutal side of which you once spoke, but there's another, altogether different side to you which—which—I—like...'

Silence followed, a silence of amazement during which Rad just stared at his wife's bent head, for she found it impossible to look into his eyes. Her cheeks were hot, because of her admission, since it was a near confession of love, and because of the knowledge that her husband must be thinking of her reciprocation to his lovemaking and asking himself if it *was* love which she now felt for him. Lynn, acutely conscious of a feeling of humiliation at the idea of her inability to combat the love which had come unbidden to her, would have taken back her confession if that had been at all possible, yet at the same time she had to accept the fact that she was drawn irresistibly to him and had been almost from the first, despite her horror at the idea of being the wife of a wandering gipsy. His physical attractions were something she had not been able to ignore, his passionate nature undoubtedly suited her own.

She looked up at last, catching her breath at the softness in his eyes. And in that moment she knew that her fate was sealed, that wherever he led she would follow, whether it be to one gipsy camp after another, or perhaps something a little better. Whatever he was, whatever he did, she was bound inextricably to him... for the rest of her life.

He was speaking, softly, disbelievingly, dazedly shaking his curly head.

'If this is the truth, my Lynn, then there is hope for us—indeed there is hope for us!' The last words were spoken with deep and vibrant emphasis, and it was plain to Lynn that an unbearable burden had been lifted from his shoulders ... Or could it be his heart? Excitement surged through her so that her whole body quivered. If Rad loved her ...? If he really loved her then surely he would abandon the gipsy life and do what *she* wanted! To have a pretty little cottage, to live like normal people, to work for a living, to bring up children who would be respected by society ... It was a dream, but not an impossible one—— 'Lynn,' he said, breaking into her happy musings, 'you did mean what you said? You will never leave me—never try to run away?'

She hesitated, but only for a second or so. And then she smiled at him with her lovely eyes and said in soft and gentle tones,

'I meant it, Rad. I'll never leave you.' That was all, yet there was so much more she wanted to say. She wanted to ask him to leave this gipsy existence and live properly, but now did not seem the time and she fell silent, eating her lunch. Nor did Rad seem inclined to speak; he was contented and it showed, since never had she seen his features so relaxed, so serenely at peace.

It was almost four o'clock when the telephone rang; Rad, who had been writing letters while Lynn browsed through a magazine she had found, rose at once, murmured a word of apology, and went swiftly to the telephone. She heard him exclaim, saw his face become taut and his mouth compress. Beneath the darkness of his skin a grey tinge had appeared.

'She's ... dead?' Rad's voice was hoarse, and scarcely audible. 'No ...? Condition's grave? I must get hold of him before the police do. God, why didn't he come here, as he intended!'

Lynn, her face drained of colour and her heart racing with a fear for which the reason was totally obscure, could scarcely hold back the questions that rose to her lips as she stared at her husband, holding the receiver, listening to the voice at the other end of the line. She heard him speak again and knew what he would say to her when once the receiver was replaced on its rest.

'I must leave you for a few hours, Lynn. Please don't ask me questions, for although I'm now willing to answer them all there's no time at present. I have urgent business to attend to, but you'll be all right here, won't you? Or shall I send Mrs White to stay with you?' Clearly he was torn and Lynn said calmly that she would like to go with him. But he shook his head. 'Not this time, dear. It's not a situation in which I want you involved.' His eyes held a depth of anxiety to which Lynn had no desire to add, so she managed a faint smile and said she would be all right here, at the bungalow, but she did ask if he would be back that night. The place was so very lonely that she rather thought she might be afraid once darkness fell.

'I hope I shall be back,' he answered, but went on to add that he was by no means sure. The urgency about his manner being conveyed to Lynn resulted in her full assurance that she would manage very well, even if he did not return until the following morning.

'You're an angel,' he murmured before kissing her tenderly on the lips. 'Soon, all will be well between us; keep that in mind, dear Lynn—do please keep that in mind.' And with that he was turning away and the next moment he was in her car, driving away from the bungalow at a speed which sent the dust flying in clouds behind him.

Left alone with her multitude of confusing thoughts, Lynn stared out to the sea, so calm, so blue in the sunshine. Who was this Albán? That he was important in her husband's life was an undoubted fact. That he had committed some crime was also a fact. Rad was obviously trying to save the man from the police...

'Oh, dear, why bother my head with it all when I have no possible means of solving anything until Rad returns and gives me a full explanation?' she sighed.

Gradually dusk began to descend, painting the sea with a pearl-grey sheen and the mountains with a soft purple veil. It was an idyllic spot and Lynn decided to take a stroll later, when she had had her evening meal. But she made no attempt to prepare it, although she knew exactly what she was having. A salad and some tinned meat if Rad did not return, but something more substantial if it should turn out to be a meal for two. Meanwhile, she lighted the candles in the sitting-room, and switched on the two standard lamps. What a pleasant room it was! A room where good taste combined with wealth to create something of real beauty. She wished she and Rad could have a home like this. Perhaps one day they would, when Rad settled himself in a job. He had money, though, and once again she found herself asking the question: where did he get it from?

A sigh escaped her, then determinedly she thrust out all questions, deciding to read in order to occupy her mind for the next hour or so. It was so quiet, so lonely. It had not occurred to her that the time would drag, but it certainly was dragging, and at half-past eight she decided to prepare her meal, resigned to eating it alone as it seemed that Rad was unable to get back in time for dinner. Perhaps he would manage to get back later, though; Lynn sincerely hoped so.

After the meal she washed the dishes, then, putting on a cardigan, she took a short stroll before going to bed. The world outside was silent, sleeping under the silver glow from above. Lynn, remembering that other stroll last evening with her husband, felt impatient for him to return. He might already have returned, she thought, turning instantly to retrace her steps. But she was disappointed; the house was quiet, just as she had left it.

Within half an hour she had washed and was in bed, having extinguished all the lights, and soon she drifted into a peaceful slumber from which she was awakened by some sound which she failed to identify. Wind? The breeze had been freshening when she was outside, taking her stroll.

She lay there, wanting to snap on the light and yet, conversely, driven by instinct to remain totally silent, and in the darkness, which somehow seemed to be a comforting protection. The sound was not repeated and eventually she drifted once again into a peaceful sleep. But this time her sleep was short; she was again brought to wakefulness by a sound which was rather like that of a drawer being closed. Was Rad in? Of course, and he did not want to disturb her! He must be intending to sleep in one of the other bedrooms. Lynn's immediate impulse was to get up and go to him, but she was soon asking herself if *she* would be disturbing *him*. Not that he was asleep, but he might just want to be alone with his thoughts, since his mission had been a serious one. Yet Lynn's curiosity was difficult to contain; she desired nothing so much as that the mystery surrounding Rad should be cleared up as soon as possible. He had promised to explain everything, to answer all her questions. After that, everything would be all right between them. He had said this, and she had no doubts at all that she could rely on his promise being kept.

By now she was wide awake, and wished she had

brought a book to bed with her. The bedlight was close and she switched it on. Five minutes past three. A long time to go yet, so perhaps she ought to get herself something to read. There were a great number of books on a shelf in the sitting-room, and also some glossy magazines in a rack. But no, as she felt sure she would disturb her husband if she got up. As all was quiet now she presumed he had gone to bed. She snapped out the light and settled down again, but it was a long time before she slept, and even when she did manage to doze it was fitfully, and by five o'clock she was once again wide awake.

'Shall I disturb Rad if I get up now?' she was asking herself as she lay there, staring at the lovely floor-to-ceiling drapes through which the sunlight was penetrating. 'Perhaps I'd better wait a while; after all, it was very late when he got to bed.'

So she waited until half-past six, then rose quietly and went along to have her bath. The water was allowed to run until the bath was nearly full, and she lay in it for a quarter of an hour or so, her thoughts with her husband, her one wish being that his mission had come to a satisfactory conclusion and that Albán had at last been contacted.

After drying and powdering herself Lynn slipped into her negligé and came out of the bathroom, her glance wandering along the passage as she wondered which bedroom Rad was occupying.

And then a door opened and a smile leapt to her lips ... only to fade again as she looked into his face. What was the matter with him? The cruelty, the harshness she had seen on that never-to-be-forgotten day when he had attacked her were clearly written into his swarthy features.

'Rad...' she whispered disbelievingly. 'What...?'

The dressing-gown he had slipped on over his naked body had come open at the top and she saw a mass of jet black hair ... *too much hair*. Her eyes lifted and involuntarily she put up a frightened hand to her mouth. Why was he staring at her like that—as if she were some kind of an apparition! Then his black eyes wandered and she coloured hotly, so insulting was his glance. Why didn't he speak to her? He looked like a madman and all she could think of was that brutal side of him, that 'Mr Hyde' part of him that had so often terrified her. 'Rad,' she faltered again chokingly, 'you—you—frighten me ...' Her voice trailed off and she caught her breath in a sudden jerk that racked her whole body.

This man was not her husband.

With the speed of lightning the truth flashed upon her. This was Albán, and Albán was the brother of whom Rad had spoken ... but what Rad had failed to mention was that his brother was an identical twin!

'How the devil do *you* come to be here?' he demanded at last. 'You mentioned Rad. Where is he?'

Lynn, backing away from him with the intention of securing herself in the bedroom, the door of which had a lock and key, she had noticed, made no answer. In fact, she rather thought that fear was so strong that she would not have been able to articulate words even had she wanted to do so.

The man repeated his question, advancing towards her as he did so. Her eyes dilated as she found herself against a wall that jutted out owing to the shape of the passage.

'Rad's—Rad's l-looking f-for you ...'

A sneer twisted the man's evil countenance.

'He got married, so I was told. You must be his wife.'

'That's r-right.'

'How come? I myself nearly had you once. Máda, the bitch, saved you!' He thrust his dark fingers through his hair; it had been wild and unruly before, but it was much worse now. Yes, he looked every inch a madman ... an escaped convict almost. 'She can't save you now, though,' he went on, taking another threatening step towards her. 'What a stroke of luck! A beauty for the taking, and that beauty my brother's wife! He'll be paid out at last!' The man was raving, and a slight froth covered his lower lip. Terrified, Lynn tried to scream, even while conscious of the fact that there would be no one to hear her. The sheer horror of her situation possessed her, mingling with a hundred visions which flashed into her receptive mind, visions that brought almost total enlightenment ... almost but not all. She saw again that mass of hair; knew that this had given her the first subconscious knowledge that this man was not her husband. But now there was something else, something which, had it not remained in her subconscious all this time, would have proved at once that the man who had attacked her and the man who had been leading that lovely horse were not the same. For this man had the trace of a scar on his hairline; she had not noticed it until he dragged his fingers through his black curls. She recalled being puzzled on a certain occasion when she was with Rad; she had been searching for something without knowing just what it was. Now, she knew that the scar had registered, but not consciously. If only it had! What a lot of heartache would have been saved!

'Come here, girl!' The man's coarse voice was a terrifying command. 'What have you on beneath that filmy thing? Nothing, I'll wager. Nor have I beneath this thing I borrowed from my wealthy brother.' A snarl preceded the leap he gave, a leap which brought him so close to Lynn that she was nauseated. 'What luck!' he rasped again. 'Let's hope that Rad's wild goose chase keeps him away for another hour or so!' His hand shot forth and Lynn, almost swooning with horror and fright, began to struggle with every ounce of strength she possessed. If only she were dressed ... But as it was her struggles did little else than reveal what lay beneath the filmy covering she wore.

He had the strength of an ox, and used it. Lynn, still resisting furiously, prayed for a miracle, prayed that her husband would appear, quickly, before this brother of his could succeed with his dastardly intention. But such miracles rarely happen and very soon Lynn's strength was exhausted and she lay still while the man, lifting her up, carried her to the couch in the sitting-room. Once there, however, she seemed to become imbued with a new strength and, pushing violently against his chest, she managed to send him hurtling across the room. Vaguely she had the impression of him striking his head against the granite sill which edged the fireplace, and then all became dark as consciousness left her.

CHAPTER TEN

SHE was not out for long. Opening her eyes, she saw Albán lying there, his head in a pool of blood.

'What have I done? I think I've killed him.' Although nauseated she managed to slide a hand to his heart, and gave a deep sigh of relief. He was breathing. 'I must get a doctor.' She found the telephone book in a drawer, but no sooner had she opened it than she wondered if this was what her husband would have wanted her to do. She was incredibly calm now, as if nature, by robbing her of consciousness for that short time, had worked its own medicatrix and restored her nerves to normal. Certainly her mind was clear, so clear that when she saw Albán move her one thought was to render him harmless. Not that she believed he could rally, but it could be possible. If she were to be here with him for any length of time she wanted him tied up!

She tied his hands, with a cord she cut from a sunblind in the kitchen, then, after getting dressed, she bathed his head, relieved to discover that the wound he had received was not serious. He opened his eyes eventually and stared uncomprehendingly at her. Then he looked at his hands and frowned.

'Who are you?' he asked. 'Where am I?'

'I'm your brother's wife,' she told him quietly, her chief emotion being—strangely indeed—one of pity. The man was in pain both physically and mentally.

'Who tied me up like this?' he snarled, tugging at the cord that held his hands together.

'I did. You attacked me. I pushed you and you fell

against the curb here. I've bathed your head; the gash isn't deep. I expect it'll soon heal.'

He was silent for a space, taking all this in.

'Thwarted a second time, was I? It would have been a victory if I could have taken Rad's bride——' He broke off, his face twisting as a spasm of pain shot through his head. 'Where's Rad?' he asked eventually.

'Looking for you,' replied Lynn patiently. 'I've already told you.'

'He'll come back here!' There was an urgent note in his voice as he added, 'He mustn't find me! Undo this blasted cord or I'll kick the daylights out of you!' He was struggling to his feet and Lynn wished she had done a more thorough job of tying him up. But she had wanted to bathe the wound, fearful that it might be serious. 'I said, untie this cord!' He staggered to his feet, took a few steps forward, then fell full length on to the carpet. Lynn bit her lip, compassion sweeping over her. What a sorry sight he was! A man of such wonderful physique, of such attraction, to be lying there, helpless, blood oozing from the gash on his head. His hands were filthy, his nails bitten down to the quick. His mouth twisted convulsively as he turned his head towards where Lynn was standing, and that froth she had noticed previously appeared again. So many things came back to her as she stood there, looking down at him, but standing out above all were the words of Olave when he stated that this was the life which Albán had chosen. Rad had replied vehemently that it was not the life he should be leading; he had wanted to help him, to give him self-respect.

'Rad wants to talk to you,' she said, watching as he swung himself on to his back. 'It will be to your advantage to see him.'

'What's he told you? I'll wager he didn't own up to

robbing me of what should have been mine? I'm the elder! He was lucky, though—he was taken by our grandparents. They didn't know there were two of us, so he was made the heir and even took their name——' He stopped and sat up, his brow creasing in pain. Lynn asked him if he would like some tablets, but he shook his head. 'Taken from the gipsies when he was sixteen and brought up as a gentleman, he was! Because those damned grandparents suddenly had conscience trouble over their treatment of our mother—throwing her out because she ran off with a gipsy! Cut her out of their will and even flew a black flag from the Abbey, just to let everyone know that as far as they were concerned she was dead! Then long after she *was* dead they decided to make amends—but they didn't——'

'Flew a black flag...' murmured Lynn dazedly. 'What abbey are you referring to?' She needed no answer, of course; she knew now who her husband was.

'Ballytara Abbey, of course! You don't need me to tell you you're married to the owner of one of the most noble houses of Ireland! Owner,' he spat out, glowering at her. 'I'm the owner—I, not he!'

'Calm yourself,' advised Lynn—but she herself was trembling all over, her mind chaotic, her whole nervous system affected by what she was hearing. That beautiful girl of the portrait was Rad's mother; de Gais was his name, a most noble name which, Albán had said, had been taken by his brother—obviously to please his grandparents, those people who had so callously cut their daughter right out of their lives.

'I must leave here before he comes! I've been dodging him too long to be caught now! I shall disgrace him yet! Do you know something, girl?' His voice was low, guttural. His head was bent and his black eyes glittering with a sort of insane expression. 'I've nearly killed Máda! I hoped I'd killed her, but she's as tough as hell! I wanted to frighten Rad, to let him live with the knowledge that he's the brother of a murderer! I want to injure him so he'll never get over it——' Albán stopped suddenly, glancing towards the window. Lynn, who had already heard the car, ran to open the door for her husband. One look at his face told of his bitter disappointment at the failure of his mission, and it was with a happy feeling in her heart that she was able to say,

'Rad, your brother's here!'

'Albán?' He looked curiously at her. 'I'll go to him,' he said, and went past her into the sitting-room.

'Blast that girl!' she heard Albán say. 'If she hadn't run to that door I'd have been away—out through the back and into the hills! Well, my *gentleman* brother! What have you to say to me now you've caught up with me? Say it and let me be gone! I've no wish to stay under this roof a moment longer than necessary!'

'You've stayed under it many times. It's always been your right to stay here, or at the Abbey for that matter——' Rad stopped abruptly. 'What's wrong with your head—and your hands?' he asked frowningly. Lynn was standing in the doorway and she waited with interest to see what Albán would say. She saw him leer in some amusement, then gnash his teeth.

'I frightened your bride—was going to have a bit of fun with her at your expense, but by a stroke of luck she managed to put me out of action long enough to tie my hands, blast her!'

As Rad turned Lynn saw the deep crimson threads running up the sides of his mouth.

'What happened?' he demanded, eyes narrowed. 'Did he hurt you?'

'Hadn't time,' broke in Albán before Lynn could reply. 'Got her on the couch, but that was all. She'd got nothing on, hardly. What a missed opportunity! She pushed me against the fender!'

Rad's fists closed and he stepped forward. Fury raged within him and Lynn, fearing he would do his brother some irreparable injury, stepped forward and took one of his hands in hers.

'Don't, Rad,' she pleaded. 'He needs pity, not punishment.' So gentle her voice, compassionate the expression which Rad saw in her eyes. His own eyes became tender, and if he heard the sneering exclamation uttered by his brother he chose to ignore it as he said,

'I see you've had a fright, my love. But thank God you've not been harmed!' He turned to Albán. 'That girl's gravely ill,' he said.

'I'd hoped she was dead! I came here to escape the police, not thinking you'd be here.'

'Olave told me you were coming. What time did you arrive?'

When Albán told him Rad turned to his wife.

'I thought it was you,' she said. 'And although I wanted to come to you I didn't, because I felt you might not want to be disturbed.'

'You took it for granted that I was using another room, obviously?'

'That's right.' Lynn said no more than this, but Albán, after persuading Rad to untie his hands, became expansive and within two or three minutes Rad knew all that had happened since his brother's arrival. Lynn, watching Rad's face, saw a muscle pulsate in his throat, knew that in imagination he was seeing just what might have happened had she not had the incredibly good fortune to catch Albán off his guard for a moment.

'So you know a little about me,' Rad was saying as he turned again to his wife.

She nodded, and a flush of guilt rose to tint her cheeks.

'I've been awful with you,' she said.

'Not as awful as I've been with you, my dear.'

She glanced at the scar and said,

'I now know a little about you, as you just said, but *you* don't yet know everything.' Her glance went to Albán, who was now sitting on the couch, his head in his hands. All the fight seemed to have gone out of him and Lynn strongly suspected that, if he should raise his head, she would see tears in his eyes. 'Shall I leave you, Rad? You'll be wanting to have a long talk with your brother. I'll be in the kitchen, preparing lunch ...' She tailed off as Rad shook his head.

'I rather think it will be easier if you stay,' he said. 'It will save a great deal of explaining later.'

'But surely it's a private matter?'

'I have nothing now that I want to keep from my wife,' he rejoined simply, and Lynn felt her heart lift with happiness.

She sat down on a chair by the window, her eyes meeting those of Albán when presently he looked across at her.

'Well,' began Rad in that finely-timbred voice of his, 'it's a pretty dance you've led me, Albán. However, that's in the past now and all I want is for you to accept your half-share——'

'No! I've been robbed and I shall take nothing!'

Lynn had been right, Albán was crying; the tears ran unchecked down his brown cheeks.

Rad, turning to Lynn, began to explain just how it

was that he alone had come into the de Gais fortune and the house. His mother—a mere child at the time—had eloped with a handsome member of a tribe of gipsies who had camped close to the Abbey grounds. She was cut off by her parents and even though she wrote to tell them that she was expecting a child they did not reply.

'Of course, she had no idea she was having twins,' continued Rad quietly. He was standing with his back to the fireplace, with both his listeners sitting facing him, their expressions attentive. 'She died giving birth to us, and as our father had already deserted her we were given over to foster-parents and, unfortunately, separated in the process.'

'How very sad,' murmured Lynn almost to herself.

'Sad for me, not him!' flashed Albán viciously. 'I was put with a couple who didn't care a damn about me, while he went to a woman whose husband and son had died within a year of one another. She doted on this child she was given, and pompously gave him the name of Radulf because, she said, it was a name used by the nobility and therefore was most fitting.' A sneer edged his voice and his mouth twisted evilly. 'She maintained, too, that he was the elder, but that was a lie!'

'It was never established which of us was the elder,' began Rad, when his brother interrupted him.

'Teresa and Austin, who took me, told me that I was born first!'

'Well, I can't argue that point, Albán, because, as I've said, we can't prove which of us is the elder.'

'I am the elder!'

It was obvious, decided Lynn, that Albán had a chip on his shoulder because, convinced that he was the elder, he had not come into the inheritance.

Ignoring what Albán said, Rad went on to explain to Lynn that although a friend of his, Olave, knew from the beginning who the boys' mother was, he told no one, except the foster-parents, being convinced that their grandparents would not own them.

'But later—so rumour had it,' intervened Albán, 'Olave would have liked to contact them, as he wanted you to be a gentleman! Decided you had so much of our mother in you that you ought not to be living in a gipsy camp.' He paused and it was Rad who took up the story.

'Olave did not contact them, though, because he knew that my foster-mother would be brokenhearted if she lost me. I'm glad he kept quiet,' added Rad pensively, and Lynn recalled hearing him telling Olave that he would have done the same himself. What a wonderful person he was!—being more concerned with his gipsy foster-mother than with the fact that he could have enjoyed the good life much earlier than he had. 'You see,' he went on, still pensive, 'she was middle-aged when she took me, and there would have been nothing in her life if I'd gone out of it. She could read and write and she made me learn these things. She gave me books, spending money on them that she could ill afford.' Rad paused a moment and the pensive look was replaced by a frown. 'But the camp life, the gipsy environment as a whole, naturally affected me. I was no gentleman at that time,' he owned, looking at his wife, 'and I've always had a vicious temper. I fear there's much of my father in me, despite what Olave thinks.'

'But much more of your mother,' put in Lynn gently, her eyes tender as they looked into his. 'Do you know, Rad, I wouldn't have you any different.'

Diverted for a space, Albán said, glancing from one to the other,

'How did you two come to meet? And how did it come about that you married so quickly? You obviously hadn't yet met Rad that day when your car broke down outside the camp.'

'Car broke down?' Rad, totally bewildered, directed his glance at Lynn. 'What's all this about?'

'Don't you know?' Albán paused a second, then burst out laughing. 'I nearly had this wench twice——'

'Be quiet!' ordered Lynn, unwilling to sit there and listen to the version which would inevitably come from a man like Albán. 'Rad, let me tell the story, please?'

'But of course,' answered her husband, frowning. 'Be quick, because all this is most bewildering. You never mentioned my brother——'

'She wouldn't!' he broke in, 'because——'

'Lynn will tell me all about it,' snapped Rad, and turned once more to her. She spoke quietly, her face pale and her heart beating a little too quickly. She left nothing out, even though Rad's expression was one of murderous intent long before she had finished speaking.

'Why, you—fiend!' he rasped. 'I ought to be strangling you, not offering to help you. You're not deserving of anything other than a prison sentence!' Rad's face was twisted and for a fleeting moment she saw only evil in his features. But then he relaxed, though it was plain that he was going to withdraw his offer of help and tell his brother to go his own way. This he did, but Lynn intervened, pleading for the man who would have ruined her. Rad shook his head at first, grimly reminding Lynn just what his brother's action had cost them both, but she renewed her plea and at last

Rad relented and said he would be willing to help his brother.

'But you can't forgive me,' sneered Albán, no sign of gratitude in his voice.

Rad looked directly at him.

'No,' he answered inexorably, 'I can't ever forgive you. You've caused both Lynn and me to treat each other abominably!'

Albán shrugged carelessly.

'I don't expect you'd explain even if I asked you, which I shall not. Whatever you've done to one another is plainly forgotten now,' he declared. 'What puzzles me is how the wench didn't come to know there were two of us——' He stopped, laughed, then continued, 'Of course! The swell from Ballytara Abbey wouldn't be over-anxious to brag that he had a brother like me! She did realise, though, this morning, that you had a twin! Lord, how funny it would have been if she'd not made the discovery, and had let me——' He got no further, as Rad, drifts of crimson surging up beneath the swarthiness of his skin, stepped forward and, dragging Albán to his feet, would have struck him across the mouth had not Lynn flung herself between them.

'Rad—no, you mustn't! Alban is to be pitied far more than blamed! Just think how unfortunate he's been compared with you. Help him, Rad, to please me.' Her eyes were actually moist as tears fought for full release. 'He is your brother, after all—your twin brother. If fate hadn't separated you then you'd both be in similar positions—whether you were rich and landed or just poor uneducated gipsies.'

Both men looked at her disbelievingly.

'You can forgive him?' said Rad.

'She's ... different,' murmured Albán. 'I've never

been used to her kind—only Máda's kind...' His eyes seemed glazed as they stared into Lynn's tear-filled ones. 'He's struck it lucky—once again.' But the sneer had gone from his mouth, the harshness from his voice. 'If I'd found someone like you...'

'You will,' Lynn assured him kindly. 'One day, Albán, someone will love you.' Her voice caught because the tears were so very close, and because her throat was blocked a little, the result of emotion. She was not sure that he could ever be kind to a girl, but she hoped he could. He was not *all* bad; how could he be with that lovely girl for a mother? She looked from him to Rad, saw the love in his eyes, and the wonderment.

'Please go on with your story,' she said, wanting only to ease a situation which had become fraught with emotion for all three of them. 'You were telling me about your foster-mother, and how she tried to educate you.'

He nodded, and picked up the story, telling Lynn that Maureen had died when he was sixteen and Olave had then written to his grandparents, who replied promptly, offering Rad a home at the Abbey. They had no other children and actually welcomed the idea of an heir since, if no near heir could have been found, the estate would have gone to a very distant relative living in America.

'He's leaving out an important part,' broke in Albán, though quietly and without rancour either in his expression or in the way he phrased his words. 'I was never sought for. Olave never even tried to find me at this time.'

'Perhaps you don't know, Albán,' said Rad, 'but Olave had heard that, when you were only a few months old, the caravan caught fire and you and your foster-parents perished in the blaze. You will know that they took you from the camp where we'd been born—and where I stayed—and took you to the far north.'

'He should have made sure, though. As it happened I was saved, sustaining no more serious injury than a small burn caused by a piece of wire falling on my forehead——' Unconsciously he lifted a hand to touch the scar which was visible only when his curly black hair was a little way back from his forehead, as when teased by the breeze or, as now, removed by his hand. 'Olave discovered I was alive only just over two years ago, and even then he waited several weeks before mentioning the fact to you. I expect he was reluctant to upset you, knowing what a rake I'd turned out to be.'

'It's about two years since he told me of your existence,' said Rad reflectively.

'And by then you'd become a gentleman, while I was still an uncouth, uneducated gipsy, having, a long time previously, got myself a second pair of foster-parents who treated me like a slave. I left them when I was twelve and I've been on my own ever since.' His lip quivered and for one agonising moment Lynn thought he was going to burst into tears. She herself was very close to weeping tears of commiseration, but she valiantly held on to her control.

'I did offer you a home,' Rad reminded his brother quietly. 'You could have come to the Abbey, begun to educate yourself, and to mix with the sort of people you should have been mixing with for a long while. You refused, and it hurt, Albán, because after all, half of everything was yours. I wanted us to be friends; we had no one else who was close.' Rad spoke with deep sorrow not untinged with regret that his brother had refused to be his friend. 'I know you declared at the time that you weren't willing to accept my charity, but you should have taken it as your *right*—which it still is. You're fully entitled to half of everything.'

What could be fairer than that? wondered Lynn, the love she had for her husband glowing in her eyes as she looked up into Rad's face. His smile came, and a tenderness seemed to take a little of the blackness from his own eyes.

'It was because I'd learned—rightly or wrongly—that I was the elder and I felt cheated, not only of the money but of an education. I wanted to be a gentleman but knew I never would be, not at my age. You, Rad, were lucky, being taken at sixteen. You'd not have found it so easy if you'd been going on for thirty, as I was at the time you made me the offer.'

Rad nodded understandingly and went on to admit that even at sixteen it had not been easy to adapt to the new life that was to be his from then on.

'As a matter of fact,' he added ruefully, 'the conventional way of life didn't particularly appeal to me, since I liked my freedom. Many were the times when I was tempted to run away and join the people I'd been brought up with.'

Lynn, listening with the deepest interest to all these things she was learning about her husband, realised just what a struggle he must have put up in order to stay at the Abbey. She strongly suspected that his grandparents were not easy to live with, nor to please. It would require tremendous strength of character, and perseverance, for a man like Rad to conform and to discipline himself most sternly not to surrender to temptation.

'If you had run off,' said Albán musingly, 'then I might have been in your shoes now.'

'Perhaps.'

Lynn frowned to herself, quite unable to imagine the uncouth Albán as the country squire. He would not know how to go on at all. But of course he knew this, and had merely put the idea forward for the sake of it.

'What I want to ask you, Albán,' said Rad, 'is whether you are now willing to accept the help I've offered, keeping in mind that it's definitely *not* charity?'

'You're offering me a home at the Abbey?'

Rad shook his head.

'That offer cannot stand, I'm afraid. You've frightened Lynn on two occasions, so she might not feel safe with you around.'

'You've no faith in my reforming, then?' And, before his brother could answer, 'You know, Rad, I shall never understand why you bothered about me—waiting at home for clues to come as to my whereabouts, then chasing off all over the place, wearing clothes which you must have hated, simply so that the gipsies wouldn't be embarrassed by the superior status of their visitor. And after all that, missing me every time, often by little more than an hour or so. Had the positions been reversed,' went on Albán frankly, 'I'd have given up, let you go to the devil by the quickest route you could find.'

Rad merely smiled faintly and made no comment. Albán looked at him, noting the fine structure of his features, the stamp of nobility, the air of the aristocrat, and suddenly he slumped forward and put his head in his hands. 'Olave was disgusted with my way of life,' he owned, 'and I'm surprised that he mentioned me to you at all. I've been a rake, a thief, a seducer. Even the gipsies have no place for me—no permanent place, that is. I'm an outcast and always will be.' His mouth quivered and Lynn thought how very different he appeared from that fiend who had meant such mischief towards her. She looked pleadingly at her husband, heard him utter words that were running through her own mind at that very moment.

'You're your own worst enemy, Albán. Why don't you turn over a new leaf? You once mentioned to Olave that you could, if you had some money, go into partnership with a man who had emigrated to Australia and started a timber business. Does the offer still hold, do you think?'

'I don't know ... I should think so, because the last I heard of him was that he was considering folding up through lack of finance.'

'The finance will be no problem.'

'I think perhaps I shall go out there.'

Lynn caught her breath; she glanced at her husband and saw the total relaxing of his features as satisfaction swept over them.

'Soon, Albán?'

His brother nodded, saying yes, he was quite willing to go soon.

'You'll accept half of everything?' asked Rad.

'The de Gais fortune and the Abbey were bequeathed to you.'

'That's of no matter. Half is yours by right.'

'I'll not take half at present. I don't feel I'm fitted to handle a large fortune, Rad. Give me what's required for this partnership and keep the rest safe for me. I'll come to you if I need it.'

'If that's what you want. I'll invest it for you, Albán——' Rad broke off as the telephone bell rang, and his face became grave as he turned and went over to pick up the receiver. Lynn, watching his expression closely, felt her spirits lift as she saw it change.

He turned in a moment and said,

'Máda's going to be all right. She's not going to make a charge.'

Albán's face remained taut. Lynn did not think he had had much joy from his association with the gipsy girl.

'I'm glad,' was all Albán said.

After a moment Rad asked him if he would take Conn to Australia with him.

'He's been in trouble, too,' went on Rad with a sudden frown, 'and I've promised to help him if he'll behave himself. He wants to emigrate...' Rad stopped as he saw Lynn's expression. 'He'd not have helped you escape,' he told her in some amusement. 'He made a confession to me, saying your offer of money almost tempted him, but he changed his mind.' Rad's eyes lit with humour. 'Aren't you glad, my love, that he did change his mind?'

'We never went back anyway.'

'No, but it so happened that he was at one of the camps at which we stayed.'

'Oh...'

'What's all this about escaping?' Albán wanted to know.

'We'll tell you another time,' promised his brother, 'when you come over on a visit.'

Albán shrugged, giving the impression that once he left here he would never return.

'Getting back to Conn,' said Rad. 'He's cut out for something better than the gipsy life and, fortunately for him, he knows it. That boy'll make good.'

'Perhaps I shall too,' said Albán unexpectedly.

'I hope so,' responded Rad fervently, and then, looking at Albán's head, 'What about a good rest? I'll get you a drink and some tablets.'

'Yes, I think that'll be a good idea.' Albán rose to his

feet unsteadily. 'Will you arrange for my passage? I don't feel up to the various tasks involved.'

'You can leave everything to me,' promised Rad. 'And now, to bed, my lad!'

Ten minutes later Lynn was alone with her husband, on the verandah, with the calm Atlantic spreading away to the clear dark line of the horizon.

'Well, my precious one, there doesn't appear to be much that hasn't been cleared up, does there?'

Lynn shook her head, merely saying,

'I do hope Albán makes good.'

'You're generous, after what he did to you.' Rad looked at her, taking her hand in his. 'If only we hadn't always been at cross purposes when talking about the "first" meeting then we should never have had all those misunderstandings. I always was puzzled by your indignation when I said you should be ashamed, while you told me I was the one who should be ashamed.'

'If only I'd mentioned about the car breaking down ...' Lynn tailed off and smiled. 'So many ifs, weren't there, Rad?'

'Yes, my love. We were certainly the victims of circumstances, but we've come out unscathed.' He stared for a moment into her upturned face, then drew her gently into his arms. 'My dear wife,' he murmured, as his lips found hers. 'I knew as soon as I saw you that you were the girl for me. In fact I had said that I would know, at first sight, the girl I wanted for my wife. I'd been watching you for some time,' he went on to admit, and Lynn vividly recalled her impression that she was being watched. 'I loved you dearly, Lynn, all the time, yet hated you too, for despising me.'

She averted her head, torn apart by the idea that

after Rad had fallen in love with her on sight she had struck out at him so viciously.

'Didn't you consider it strange that I should strike you, and say such terribly insulting things—and all for no apparent reason? You must have received a dreadful shock?'

'I'll not deny that,' was Rad's grim rejoinder. 'The whole thing happened so quickly that for a few seconds I couldn't even think, then a black rage swept over me and I wanted only to make you pay. I suppose I had an inferiority complex,' he confided, 'as, you see, I've always been conscious that I must resemble my father a good deal in looks and as a result I've been aware of my gipsy background. It appeared that at your first glance you branded me a gipsy, and beneath you. You seemed to resent that fact that I would presume to speak to you and in consequence raised your crop——'

'I thought you were coming to attack me again,' broke in Lynn, deeply distressed. 'I was so terrified...' She choked over the words and Rad interrupted, saying firmly that they would not talk about it ever again.

'No,' she quivered, 'I don't want to, but—but the scar...' She touched it with her finger. 'Will it ever go, Rad, or—or are you marked for life?'

He laughed heartily and kissed her, telling her not to be absurd: of course the scar would go.

'Tomorrow, my love,' he said tenderly after a while, 'I shall take you to our home.'

'That will be wonderful!' she breathed, nestling her cheek against his shoulder, one half of her mind more than content to remain blank, but the other still occupied with the momentous happenings of the past few weeks. So much in so short a time! It was hardly believable. She thought of the first gipsy camp and asked Rad if he had paid the people to guard her. He said yes, and they would never have let her escape. 'They were filled with respect for you,' she said. And then, peeping up at him, 'Supposing they had let me escape?' She was frowning suddenly and so was he, but soon they were both laughing and no words were required. Then she asked about his various wild goose chases after his brother. 'Had you really been trying for two years to find him?' she wanted to know.

'On and off, but of course I had the estate to see to; I couldn't leave it for too long at a time. I used my own car, of course, except on that occasion when I used the horse, as the camp I was visiting was so close to my home.'

'I expect,' she said mischievously, 'that you dared not let me see your car?'

He laughed and agreed.

'It's a very large and luxurious car, which you will learn to drive, my love.'

'Why did you want to appear so rough and be like a gipsy?'

'Because you'd hurt me and I wanted to strike back. But there were so many times, my Lynn, when I wanted to tell you who I really was. But somehow I was stubborn, wanting you to love me for myself.'

Lynn, twisting in his arms, lifted her lips invitingly.

'I learned to love you for yourself,' she whispered huskily. 'And I'm glad that you knew before your real identity was known to me.'

'I believe you discovered your feelings one day in the car,' he said, and his glance was a challenge.

'That's true, but I meant to fight my love, Rad, because the gipsy life was not for me and—and my children.'

'But you couldn't fight it?'

'No,' she said, 'I couldn't. I discovered that all I

wanted was you, that wherever you led I would always follow.'

'You darling!' So tender his voice, so infinitely gentle his lips on hers. 'When I was in such doubt I saw only darkness without you and that was the reason for the plan I had in mind——'

'Oh, yes, the plan,' broke in Lynn curiously. 'What was it?'

'I couldn't face life without you, Lynn, and yet I knew you'd always want to get away if things continued as they were regarding our relationship. So, rather than lose you—for this I must do once you were at my home where there were servants—I thought to keep you with me by allowing you to go your own way. I'd give you a home, a generous allowance, and there'd be no obligations at all. We could meet at meal times if that was your wish, but for everything else—well, I'd not ask anything from you.'

Lynn thought about this, aware that once he did take her to the Abbey, she had an immediate chance of escape, since he could scarcely lock her up, with, as he himself had said, servants about.

'Well,' she said at last in a rather disparaging tone of voice, 'I think it was the stupidest plan I've ever heard in the whole of my life.'

'You do? Why?' he asked, looking slightly put out.

'Neither of us would have kept to it. You know very well that one day you'd have tired of the silly plan and coerced me into—into—er...' She tailed off, flushing and averting her eyes.

'I would?' he said in some amusement. 'And you, my dearest love, what would you have done to make my plan go all awry?'

For a long moment she could not voice what was in

her mind, but at last she gathered sufficient courage and said,

'I'd have wanted you, Rad, so I'd have—er—tempted you.'

Her husband raised his eyebrows at this confession and, because she had bent her head, he lifted it again with a forefinger under her chin.

'You would, eh? Er—would you care to give me a demonstration at this present moment? You see, I'm curious to know just what I'm in for——'

'Don't be so horrid!' she protested, but at the same time her eyes and her mouth were exceedingly provocative.

'I see...' murmured her husband, and before she had time to realise his intention Lynn was swept into a vortex of passion that left her breathless and the blood pounding in her head.

'Oh, dear,' she gasped, 'I must be careful in future!'

'Very careful, my love!'

They laughed together, and with his arm about her Rad led her from the verandah into the garden, where they strolled along towards the swimming-pool and the lovely shrubbery that bordered it. Here he stopped, telling her that they would come to the bungalow two or three times a year, if only to recapture memories.

'For it was here, my precious darling, that we really found one another.'

Lynn laid her head against his breast, saying nothing, but thinking again of all that had happened to her since that meeting with Rad in the woods. She had really guessed that this bungalow was his—since it was more than mere coincidence that he was so at home here, and with the clothes he wore fitting him to perfection. Yet she could not conceive how he could own so luxurious a property. She thought of many other things, such as the travelling they had done together while Rad was chasing after his brother. He must have been terribly worried that she would get away. He had driven at speed, she recalled, avoiding towns all the time. He had always got one of the gipsies to fill up the car with petrol for him, had always stopped for their picnic meals in the most lonely places he could find. How anxious he was not to lose her! She said after a while, not looking into his face,

'Are we really married, Rad?'

'According to gipsy law, yes.'

'And to the laws of the country?'

He hesitated a moment.

'I'm sure,' he said, 'that we would both be happy to be married in church.'

Lynn said no more; she would never know whether she had been legally married and she did not want to know. The church ceremony was the one she would remember all her life.

Rad was speaking, saying that the answers to her letters would be waiting for her at the Abbey. She smiled at the memory of being forced to write those letters. How she had rebelled! And she had been so curious to know what address was printed on the top of the expensive notepaper Rad had given her. She laughed softly and said,

'You won't have to stand over me when I answer them.'

'No?'

'No, because I shall write something to which you can't possibly object. I shall tell them,' she went on, 'that I'm married to the most wonderful man in the world!'

'Is that really what you think, my darling?' Rad was so serious all at once and she knew of his anxiety as in memory she saw him before the mirror, looking at his swarthy complexion, his unruly hair that would always curl, no matter what he did with it. 'Am I your true ideal, as you are mine?'

For answer Lynn merely looked up at him, her beloved vagabond, and all the love she felt for him was written in her eyes. With a little exclamation that came from the very heart of him Rad gathered her closely into his arms and, bending his head, took of his fill the sweetness of her softly-parted lips.

Harlequin Plus

A WORD ABOUT THE AUTHOR

For Anne Hampson, writing is more than just a livelihood. It is also an exciting hobby. Time and again she travels to foreign shores, where she mingles with the people who live there, gets to know them and even consigns a few interviews to tape. She takes a great many snapshots, buys dozens of postcards and collects maps of the area. Then, when she returns home to England, she makes notes, files them according to category and begins to write.

But long before Anne became a published author, she led a varied and often challenging existence, gathering a wealth of experiences along the way. Her working life began when she was very young—she left school at fourteen—and she has done everything from running a café to delivering milk at five-thirty in the morning. This last job was arranged so that she could return to school, a teacher-training college, as a "mature" student. And before deciding to write full-time, Anne taught for a number of years.

Anne Hampson likes to describe herself as a collector; not only of maps and picture postcards, but of rocks, fossils, antiques and experiences.